CW00705400

LEARNING FROM EXPERIENCE

A woman's guide to getting older without panic

PATRICIA ('PADDY') O'BRIEN lectured for over ten years at Southampton Art College. She now teaches yoga and runs a personnel training consultancy designing programmes on stress management, women's development and time management. She is also the author of *Managing Two Careers – how to survive as a working mother*. (Sheldon 1989).

Paddy O'Brien is married with five children.

Overcoming Common Problems Series

Beating Job Burnout
DR DONALD SCOTT

Beating the Blues
SUSAN TANNER AND JILLIAN BALL

Being the Boss
STEPHEN FITZSIMON

Birth Over Thirty
SHEILA KITZINGER

Body Language
How to read others' thoughts by their gestures
ALLAN PEASE

Bodypower
DR VERNON COLEMAN

Bodysense
DR VERNON COLEMAN

Calm Down
How to cope with frustration and anger
DR PAUL HAUCK

Comfort for Depression
JANET HORWOOD

Common Childhood Illnesses
DR PATRICIA GILBERT

Complete Public Speaker
GYLES BRANDRETH

Coping Successfully with Your Child's Asthma
DR PAUL CARSON

Coping Successfully with Your Child's Skin Problems
DR PAUL CARSON

Coping Successfully with Your Hyperactive Child
DR PAUL CARSON

Coping Successfully with Your Irritable Bowel
ROSEMARY NICOL

Coping with Anxiety and Depression
SHIRLEY TRICKETT

Coping with Cot Death
SARAH MURPHY

Coping with Depression and Elation
DR PATRICK McKEON

Coping with Stress
DR GEORGIA WITKIN-LANOIL

Coping with Suicide
DR DONALD SCOTT

Coping with Thrush
CAROLINE CLAYTON

Curing Arthritis – The Drug-Free Way
MARGARET HILLS

Curing Arthritis Diet Book
MARGARET HILLS

Curing Coughs, Colds and Flu – The Drug-Free Way
MARGARET HILLS

Curing Illness – The Drug-Free Way
MARGARET HILLS

Depression
DR PAUL HAUCK

Divorce and Separation
ANGELA WILLANS

The Dr Moerman Cancer Diet
RUTH JOCHEMS

The Epilepsy Handbook
SHELAGH McGOVERN

Everything You Need to Know about Adoption
MAGGIE JONES

Everything You Need to Know about Contact Lenses
DR ROBERT YOUNGSON

Everything You Need to Know about Osteoporosis
ROSEMARY NICOL

Everything You Need to Know about Shingles
DR ROBERT YOUNGSON

Everything You Need to Know about Your Eyes
DR ROBERT YOUNGSON

Family First Aid and Emergency Handbook
DR ANDREW STANWAY

Overcoming Common Problems Series

Feverfew
A traditional herbal remedy for migraine and arthritis
DR STEWART JOHNSON

Fight Your Phobia and Win
DAVID LEWIS

Getting Along with People
DIANNE DOUBTFIRE

Goodbye Backache
DR DAVID IMRIE WITH COLLEEN DIMSON

Helping Children Cope with Divorce
ROSEMARY WELLS

Helping Children Cope with Grief
ROSEMARY WELLS

How to be a Successful Secretary
SUE DYSON AND STEPHEN HOARE

How to Be Your Own Best Friend
DR PAUL HAUCK

How to Control your Drinking
DRS W. MILLER AND R. MUNOZ

How to Cope with Stress
DR PETER TYRER

How to Cope with Tinnitus and Hearing Loss
DR ROBERT YOUNGSON

How to Cope with Your Child's Allergies
DR PAUL CARSON

How to Cure Your Ulcer
ANNE CHARLISH AND DR BRIAN GAZZARD

How to Do What You Want to Do
DR PAUL HAUCK

How to Enjoy Your Old Age
DR B. F. SKINNER AND M. E. VAUGHAN

How to Get Things Done
ALISON HARDINGHAM

How to Improve Your Confidence
DR KENNETH HAMBLY

How to Interview and Be Interviewed
MICHELE BROWN AND GYLES BRANDRETH

How to Love a Difficult Man
NANCY GOOD

How to Love and be Loved
DR PAUL HAUCK

How to Make Successful Decisions
ALISON HARDINGHAM

How to Move House Successfully
ANNE CHARLISH

How to Pass Your Driving Test
DONALD RIDLAND

How to Say No to Alcohol
KEITH McNEILL

How to Spot Your Child's Potential
CECILE DROUIN AND ALAIN DUBOS

How to Stand up for Yourself
DR PAUL HAUCK

How to Start a Conversation and Make Friends
DON GABOR

How to Stop Feeling Guilty
DR VERNON COLEMAN

How to Stop Smoking
GEORGE TARGET

How to Stop Taking Tranquillisers
DR PETER TYRER

How to Stop Worrying
DR FRANK TALLIS

Hysterectomy
SUZIE HAYMAN

If Your Child is Diabetic
JOANNE ELLIOTT

Jealousy
DR PAUL HAUCK

Learning to Live with Multiple Sclerosis
DR ROBERT POVEY, ROBIN DOWIE AND GILLIAN PRETT

Overcoming Common Problems Series

Living Alone – A Woman's Guide
LIZ McNEILL TAYLOR

Living Through Personal Crisis
ANN KAISER STEARNS

Living with Grief
DR TONY LAKE

Living with High Blood Pressure
DR TOM SMITH

Loneliness
DR TONY LAKE

Making Marriage Work
DR PAUL HAUCK

Making the Most of Loving
GILL COX AND SHEILA DAINOW

Making the Most of Yourself
GILL COX AND SHEILA DAINOW

Managing Two Careers
How to survive as a working mother
PATRICIA O'BRIEN

Meeting People is Fun
How to overcome shyness
DR PHYLLIS SHAW

Menopause
RAEWYN MACKENZIE

The Nervous Person's Companion
DR KENNETH HAMBLY

Overcoming Fears and Phobias
DR TONY WHITEHEAD

Overcoming Shyness
A woman's guide
DIANNE DOUBTFIRE

Overcoming Stress
DR VERNON COLEMAN

Overcoming Tension
DR KENNETH HAMBLY

Overcoming Your Nerves
DR TONY LAKE

The Parkinson's Disease Handbook
DR RICHARD GODWIN-AUSTEN

Say When!
Everything a woman needs to know about alcohol and drinking problems
ROSEMARY KENT

Self-Help for your Arthritis
EDNA PEMBLE

Sleep Like a Dream – The Drug-Free Way
ROSEMARY NICOL

Solving your Personal Problems
PETER HONEY

Someone to Love
How to find romance in the personal columns
MARGARET NELSON

A Special Child in the Family
Living with your sick or disabled child
DIANA KIMPTON

Stress and your Stomach
DR VERNON COLEMAN

Think Your Way to Happiness
DR WINDY DRYDEN AND JACK GORD(

Trying to Have a Baby?
Overcoming infertility and child loss
MAGGIE JONES

What Everyone Should Know about Drugs
KENNETH LEECH

Why Be Afraid?
How to overcome your fears
DR PAUL HAUCK

Women and Depression
A practical self-help guide
DEIDRE SANDERS

You and Your Varicose Veins
DR PATRICIA GILBERT

Your Arthritic Hip and You
GEORGE TARGET

Overcoming Common Problems

LEARNING FROM EXPERIENCE

A woman's guide to getting older without panic

Patricia O'Brien

SHELDON PRESS
LONDON

First published in Great Britain in 1991
Sheldon Press, SPCK, Marylebone Road, London NW1 4DU

© Patricia O'Brien 1991

All rights reserved. No part of this book may be reproduced or transmitted in any form or by any means, electronic or mechanical, including photocopying, recording, or by any information storage and retrieval system, without permission in writing from the publisher.

British Library Cataloguing in Publication Data
O'Brien, Patricia
Learning from experience. – (Overcoming common problems).
1. Great Britain. Women, 30 years –
I. Title II. Series
305.48

ISBN 0–85969–620–0

Photoset by Deltatype Ltd, Ellesmere Port, Cheshire
Printed in Great Britain by Courier International Ltd, Tiptree, Essex

Contents

Acknowledgements

I would like to thank all the women who, in groups and in individual interviews, shared their personal reactions to and strategies for ageing.

Thanks to friends young and old for many interesting discussions on the subject and to Mandy Frost for the swift typing.

Thanks as always to Tim and the children for their love and support.

1

'Not Being Seventeen'

A prolonged period of one's life lived as a 'middle-aged' or 'old' woman is a fairly new deal. Until the twentieth century women could expect to die up to twenty years earlier than what is now regarded as a 'natural' span of life. Assailed by disease and hazardous childbirth, fed less in quantity and quality and, with the exception of the upper classes, worn out by much arduous physical work, ageing and death happened earlier and more swiftly, more commonly in a woman's forties or fifties, than in her sixties, seventies, or eighties.

Now, a woman in the affluent West knows that unless environmental disaster, war, or personal accident intervenes, she can hope to live into her seventies and beyond. To all intents and purposes this gives her an extra third of a life added on, a joyful opportunity certainly, but also a challenge, to know how to spend the time well and enjoyably, to find rôles and a style that will keep her well grounded in her own identity, clear in her place in the world.

From the midpoint of my own life I look ahead to perhaps another thirty-five years and wonder with some dismay where I will find the inspiration and the information I need to do it well. At first glance there seems to be a choice between spending years either as a superannuated barbie doll or as a frump. While I certainly don't intend to spend the second half of my life concentrating solely on my own ageing process, I feel I need to do some thinking about ageing, so that as it is happening I don't fall into too much needless negativity or too much avoidable floundering into the unknown. The *un*avoidable floundering with the unknown I shall have to do just like everybody else. I want to age without fear and denial, and with optimism and self-respect.

In the following pages many women in or approaching the

second halves of their lives share reflections on being a woman moving through different ages. These women range in age from thirties to seventies; some are working in the home and some out of it, some feel anxious and oppressed about aspects of their ageing process, and some feel comfortable and assured. We began by trying to pinpoint when our own increasing age first became an issue to us.

Somewhere in my late twenties I suddenly noticed I wasn't seventeen any longer. Like many other people I didn't really feel any different *inside* between the ages of about seventeen and twenty-seven. I don't even know the number of my chronological age all that accurately, I was a young woman, and if anyone asked how old I was at any particular moment I wouldn't necessarily know. Apart from the waxing and waning of the menstrual cycle and the larger waxings and wanings of pregnancies and births my body didn't change much; my hair, long and luxuriant, didn't need anything particular doing to it to look lovely, and it was obvious what clothes to wear. I did not always have enough money or feel thin enough for the clothes I wanted, but I knew well enough how to identify what they were and confined my anxieties to wondering how and when I would be thin enough and rich enough to get my hands on them.

However, a number of things creep up on you as you reach your twenty-seventh year. Twenty-seven isn't just twenty-something unspecified, it's coming close to thirty. You realize that even you will one day reach the geriatric age of thirty and even older. Remember how old people in their thirties seemed when you were eighteen? You wonder if you are the exception that proves the rule, and realize that you probably are not. Events begin to underline this feeling.

The woman who wins Wimbledon is younger than you. The woman being named businesswoman of the year is younger than you. All sorts of key people who you thought were proper grown-ups when you were only young, are younger than you. The policemen look like children dressed up, the doctor is ridiculously juvenile. I remember arriving to give a lecture at a hospital and looking aghast at the audience. They seemed to me to be delightful young people of fourteen or fifteen or so. In fact they were all fully qualified midwives and therefore must have been into their early twenties. I was older than I had understood.

Many of the women interviewed mentioned the significance of authority figures and professionals starting to look young as marker points letting them know they were 'not seventeen'.

This is funny in an edgy sort of way at a superficial level, but the implications slowly sank in. When the woman who wins Wimbledon is younger than oneself it is unlikely that one's own fantasy of being suddenly discovered as a late-developing tennis superstar will come true. This means all sorts of other fantasies about suddenly being discovered as a brilliant natural dancer, gymnast, actress, jazz singer, poet, film producer, entrepreneur, and so on move from being pleasant fantasies that might just happen, to lost dreams. One realizes that some of the paths one has taken have been exclusive of other paths one might have taken, and that one has deliberately or accidentally practised and developed certain skills both in one's professional and private life, and *not* practised and developed others. Until one's late twenties it feels as though everything is fluid, most options could still, with a bit of determination, be open, there is always a possibility of change; but after that, some possibilities are gone forever, although one can, I hope, make productive and creative change right through one's entire life.

You can't be a 'young mother' again (or if you haven't had children yet, you can't be one at all). You can't be Young Investigator of the Year or Amazing Young Artist Discovered in Suburbia or (does it all go back to Angela Brazil?) Girl Explorer in Himalayan Breakthrough, or any of that: and the sickening thing is that some people can and there they are in your office, in your family, on the TV news, flaunting their young talentedness at you.

It isn't enough to be *promising* any more. You have to have something to show for your efforts in the world. One of the extremely difficult things for women is that this phase often begins while we are occupied with looking after young children as well as trying to hang onto our careers and our own personal identities. It is important to recognize, respect, and perhaps to share our true sense of loss in letting go of some of our dreams, and some of our possible selves, some of the paths we might have taken and the things we might have been. It is also important to review and value what we *have* achieved. It may be necessary to find names and definitions for achievements which are the kind women manage all the time but which don't have proper names – and also to acknowledge that for many women enduring and surviving in this society is an achievement in itself. Look at the exercises at the end of this chapter for ways of beginning to focus your mind on these points, and ways of forming new patterns of awareness about your own life and experience.

If your children were born when you were young, they won't be leaving home when you are twenty-seven, but they might be starting to leave when you're thirty-seven, and a similar impasse may happen when your sense of personal achievement has rested on managing multiple commitments with competence and flair, and then when the children leave, your working life and your inner life, both once adapted to fit round them, look and feel thin and sketchy.

If you are without children, but you do want to have them eventually, the middle thirties is a time of growing pressure, as you realize only a finite number of fertile cycles remain to you, and your spectrum of choice is narrowing.

Women approaching the midpoint of their lives without children feel with extra poignancy what we all experience – dismay and concern about physical ageing, having to confront the finite nature of our organism. For women this is an issue relating to fertility, to power, to style and self-image, and to fear of death.

Fertility and our feelings about it are discussed fully in Chapter 4: the ambiguity beginning at this middle place is that one may be almost equally worried about becoming pregnant unexpectedly as one is about losing one's fertility forever.

Style and self-image are challenged too. Whereas in my twenties I wanted a different figure and a different bank balance, now I'm not too sure what I want. I do know that somewhere around twenty-seven I started not trying on certain kinds of clothes because they wouldn't be appropriate on me any more. I felt rebellious and inadequate – was this the beginning of a decline into frumptitude, could I strike a blow for freedom by buying a ra-ra skirt? No, I couldn't. Certain kinds of frivolous effervescent fashion have, for me at least, an age-related cutoff point, and once I reached that cutoff point I felt excluded and threatened.

About eight or nine years after I fully understood that I couldn't wear a ra-ra skirt my eldest son began to get involved with girls. A succession of dazzling nymphs, effortlessly beautiful, started to walk through the door. I began to try and cope with the fact that my house was full of young women who wore faded, knackered, jumble-sale clothes, borrowed, torn, and patched; that they mussed their hair up and stuck a slide through it crookedly, and they looked just lovely. With a far greater investment of money and time I could never look like that again – smooth and careless, and *young*. It was in vain to rationalize that experience and the tracks of time and childbirth on my face and body made for a different kind of loveliness – what I was struggling with was the fact that I did not have a choice, I could never look like that again. I could not *be seventeen*. I wonder how much nastiness from older women towards younger women is related to this shock to the older women's system? I tried not to hate these young women. Usually I failed.

Coping with the effortless beauty of younger women is a very personal issue, and we each need our own strategy to do this, but an awareness, a sense of humour, and a quite complex development in our own self-esteem can make a positive difference. Hazel, speaking at the age of fifty-two, mentioned a change in her colouring forcing her into an unwelcome change of style:

> I was always a beatnik – I was very happy with that style. I wore lots of trousers, and big loose high-necked sweaters, and lots of black. I loved the drama of black, and I was blonde and had the colouring to suit it. I was fed up to find that after my menopause the balance of my skin colour and my hair colour meant that I looked very muddy and dingy in black and just couldn't wear it any more. But now I can wear *purple*. [She said this with contempt]. Who on earth wants to wear *purple*.

For a discussion of style and ageing, see Chapter 5, where women explain how they have adapted their own style to express themselves and enjoy their clothes and appearance.

Physical changes, which clearly happen gradually throughout our lives, may pass some critical point where we suddenly can't ignore them any more, and they mark our passing into another phase. Three examples of physical change which have drawn the woman's attention forcefully to the progress of her own ageing are described here by Hazel, Christina, and Susan.

Hazel notes that 'My jawline suddenly went. It had been clearly defined and continuous, but it started to show droops and slack contours. My muscle tone went generally in my body too. My outline became less definite. Around my abdomen there was a slackness that there never used to be.'

Christina, a computer analyst of thirty-two, noticed this process beginning when she began to think about the impact of ageing upon her own self. 'I've always had a stomach that was absolutely flat, in spite of two children,' she said, 'but I'm just beginning to realize that I'm going to have to both watch what I eat and how I exercise if I want to stay that way. It's hard to define but I can feel it beginning to give a bit.'

Susan (a therapist and counsellor of fifty-four) spoke about facial hair, which in our culture is a kind of ghastly joke and deeply reviled on women, even though it is normal, and its increase as one ages is normal. Having 'too much' facial hair causes dreadful anguish and a completely unfair feeling of humiliation for some women. How often society makes us ashamed of our bodies when they are only behaving in an ordinary way and with their own integrity. Susan's point was one of those strange scenarios that cross one's mind, revealing a sense of vulnerability. 'Supposing I had an accident and I was in hospital, and a friend said to me, "Is there anything you need, shall I bring anything in for you?" – would I be too embarrassed to say "I need some tweezers?" Would anyone have the imagination to realize that I might need some?'

Maureen (Women's Officer, forty-three) also feels vulnerable about 'the fact that I dye my moustache with peroxide, also the hairs on my legs which I won't remove, but I do use peroxide and I feel that's a contradiction to my feminist principles.'

Women who identify themselves as feminist women, or women concerned with holistic health, may be very confused by their reactions to ageing. It can be difficult to disentangle these reactions which seem to be culturally conditioned, and from which, perhaps, one has made enormous efforts to deprogramme oneself, from those which are a clearer reaction of a person noticing that the body she inhabits is beginning to show signs of wear. It seemed important not to feel guilty about any reactions, but to respect them all, give them all space and time, and make choices about which to act upon after some opportunity for reflection.

Maureen has had at least three separate moments in her mid-thirties which shocked her:

> One was when I looked in the mirror and saw a line on my face that hadn't been there before. A couple of years later I looked in the mirror and definitely felt I was looking at a

> middle-aged woman. And once I just looked at the skin on my arm and thought that's different, that's changing, I'm getting older

Other women mentioned new and deeper wrinkle lines on their faces as the specific signal which marked moving into a new age for them – also a general decrease in resilience in the face which Marianne (forty) describes:

> These days if I have a late night or feel really exhausted it shows in my face, the contours sag, the lines from the sides of my nose to my mouth deepen, my eyes are puffy. I just can't stay up all night and look interestingly rumpled in the morning any more. If I stay up all night I look ancient the next day.

We look at exercise, relaxation, and loving care of our physical bodies in Chapter 3.

For Jane (thirty-five), moving into the rôle of motherhood lifted her out of a state of permanent 'seventeenness'.

> For me it was after the birth of my first child. I noticed I had some grey hairs. I felt physically changed – less attractive, and clearly no longer 'available' sexually. All that was in the past, I was a 'mum' and would not be the recipient of wolf whistles in the street. I didn't feel too bad about it – a bit sad, but also rather smug and safe.

Maureen is bisexual, and sees a difference in the effect of ageing in her sexual relationships with men as opposed to her sexual relationships with women:

> With women it makes no difference at all. I know that the relationship, the attraction, is to do with the two of us as personalities, as people, and it has nothing to do with any kind of judgement or assessment of my body. I feel the

same in a relationship with a much younger man, where there's a clear difference in our ages and I am allowed to 'be my age' because it's obviously different from his. Where I do feel anxious is with men more or less the same age as me: if things are rocky I start to look anxiously in the mirror and wonder if I appear too old. I'm caught in that contradiction again: I don't feel I *ought* to feel these things, but I do.

Knowing in our hearts as well as intellectually that our bodies are ageing, that they will one day die, is something we need to be able to feel in touch with, and, some of the time at least, to feel steady about.

That knowledge in itself immediately brings the beauty of the world up into sharp focus. Think of the cherry blossom in the spring, its delicate and fugitive beauty. Think of the few days it blooms in the tree, perfect and fragrant, and then how a windy shower will bring it all down, heaped on the pavements briefly like confetti from a carnival. I notice I have had thirty-five chances (perhaps thirty-three consciously aware chances) to see the cherry blossom. I notice I only have at the most thirty-five more chances to go. I won't ever miss it now – I won't ever forget to look.

Exercises

Throughout this book a series of exercises are suggested. The aim is to help you to work on the ideas and emotions which the material in the chapters raises. If you are not familiar with this type of exercise you may find they feel a bit artificial and peculiar at first. They are, however, useful for focusing and clarifying, and may have a particular importance for women whose habit, indeed whose necessity, may have been for decades to hold several other peoples' needs in their minds simultaneously with their own. This is a technique which helps you to be single-minded about yourself.

If you work with a partner, be careful to choose someone

you trust, to agree a bond of confidentiality about your work together, and to concentrate on helping each other to discover what your own feelings are, rather than imposing your opinions and views on each other. If you think about it carefully you will be aware that some people have a vested interest in you *not* changing. These people are not useful partners for exercises: find someone who is happy to see you change and grow.

Respect the importance of what you are doing: take the phone off the hook, don't allow arbitrary interruptions. Decide on a period of time you wish to spend (thirty minutes, one hour, two hours, or whatever), and stick to it.

Co-Counselling

Co-counselling is an informal technique for self-help which many women find useful because of its mutuality. Agree with a trusted friend a set amount of time each to spend on any issue which is important to you. While you are the 'counsellor' your contribution is in giving clear attention, clear listening, eye contact, and support. Do not interrupt, or talk about yourself, or chime in with parallel experiences. Do not give advice. Instead, give respect and space to what your partner is saying and try with brief prompts and questions to facilitate your partner's own exploration of her thoughts and feelings. Stay with the time limits you have set and when the time is up, change rôles. Co-counselling is not the same as a good chat or a heated dicussion, it is an opportunity to reflect on puzzling or challenging parts of our lives with the support of a person we trust. It is a surprisingly rich resource. For a more detailed description of co-counselling and many other self-help techniques, see Ernst and Goodison's *In Our Own Hands*, a source book for self-help therapy exercises.

Notebooks

If you don't feel like using co-counselling or if you want something to use in addition to co-counselling, it might be useful to keep a notebook. If you buy a fairly large format one you can use it for writing, drawing, and brainstorming. Buy yourself some crayons or felt-tip pens, or paints or inks too.

Use the notebook for the specific exercises in the book, and also to record the following things. Record any important thoughts that cross your mind. Write down any dreams that stay in your mind and seem to be asking for your attention. There's no need to analyse them, just write them down or illustrate them, and reflect on them; see if you can sense what that message is for you. If it isn't clear, don't worry, it sometimes takes months or years for the message of a dream to become clear. The point is just to hold it gently in your mind (or your notebook!) until it does – and to become receptive to this marvellous creative material which is arising in all of us every night of our lives. Copy into the book any poems or passages from books that move or interest you, stick into the book pictures, postcards, cards, or cuttings that help build up a picture of your inner journey.

Don't be afraid to express yourself by free drawing. We can *all* draw and until the ages of six, seven, eight or so, do so unerringly and without hesitation. Sadly, at about that time a mixture of our own frustration at not being able to make the picture on the paper the same as the picture in our mind's eye, added to other people's criticisms of our efforts, leads most of us to decide that we *can't* draw, and a great pleasure is lost from our lives forever. If you are a trained artist or designer you may have the opposite problem where your technical training and competence interfere with a free flow of imagery and expression. The way out of both these fixes to start off with, I think, is privacy combined with swiftness. Reassure yourself that nobody need see your pictures unless you want them to. Then get hold of some colours you like and doodle or scribble something quickly without thinking about it, and elaborate it as long as you like and stop as soon as you get fed up.

A notebook/scrapbook like this is useful at any period of

change or crisis in your life. A most useful one was given to me by a friend whom I rang up, in tears, one evening. I was going to have a baby and had just been on a tour of the labour ward. In spite of the midwives' efforts to humanize the rooms with plants and pictures, they remained, to anyone from outside, clinical, ugly, and overpowering with all their chrome and machinery. I could not imagine managing a sticky, messy, passionate process like giving birth in that environment.

In response to my phone call my friend sent me a scrapbook full of images of women – postcards of paintings and sculptures, pictures cut out of papers and magazines, all chosen because they showed a strong, fluid, beautiful (not fashion plate beauty, but the beauty of integrity) picture of womanhood. She included Australian cave paintings and Impressionist paintings and contemporary photographs, Hepworths, Pre-Raphaelites, and newsprint. It gave me enormous inspiration and I'm sure that taking it with me into the clinical, fearful environment of the labour ward was one of the factors that helped me to have the sticky, messy, passionate birth that I had hoped for. I have only just begun my scrapbook about women of age but look forward to it being just as empowering and just as much of a help in the experience itself (though whether I want ageing to be sticky, messy and passionate as well is something I am not yet clear about! Although it wouldn't necessarily be what everyone wants, to me it sounds like an interesting option.)

Use the three exercises below in co-counselling, free writing or drawing, or collecting images or quotations, to explore your own experience of 'not being seventeen'.

Exercise 1: Letting go of dreams

(*Do not* do this exercise on its own, do exercise 2 (page 13) *as well.*)

Think back to when you were a little girl. What were your dreams and ambitions then, what were your dreams of a job, a career, a place in the world? Write them down. What about when you were in your teenage years? What were your aspirations then? Note these down too, and add to your list any further ambitions you had as a young woman, and any that you still have now.

First, notice and celebrate the qualities and desires in yourself that led you to have these dreams and aspirations in the first palce.

Second, have a hard look at your list. Is there anything on there that is in fact still possible for you? Mark with an asterisk anything that you could, in fact, still achieve. Let the seed of that idea stay in your mind and see if you want to choose to try to achieve it. If you do, begin to do some definite action planning (see page 31).

Are there things on the list you feel clear that you will never now do – be an astronaut, run ICI, win the Olympic long jump, dance in the Royal Ballet, sail the Atlantic single-handed? Are you quite sure you will never do them? (I read recently of a woman of over sixty getting her black belt in *Tae Kwon Do*). Put a ring around the things you feel you will never do.

Spend some time on:

- enjoying the part of you that had that dream
- enjoying any ways in which, on reflection, you can see that the dream *is* fulfilled in metaphorical or analogous ways in your life as it is now (for instance you may not actually *be* a lion-tamer, but you may enjoy other kinds of risks and excitements in your actual present job
- think about letting the dream go without bitterness
- think about not letting the loss of any particular dream stop you from doing things you can do and want to do with your life.

Exercise 2: Naming achievements

Women's lives are full of acts of creativity, ingenuity, courage, endurance, and originality, which pass by without mention or acknowledgement, usually without financial reward, and often don't even have a name. There is no word for the physical and emotional strength, in a very specialist sense, required to have twenty-four months of continuous broken nights, while caring for and arranging alternative care for a baby, supporting and counselling a worried partner, doing a demanding outside-home job, and producing a continuous stream of food and laundry: yet that is an ordinary workload for women – many women are coping with extra things as well – without being appointed, named, or paid as Senior Executive Planner or Advanced Resources Co-Ordinator, or Head of Unit Development, all of which things they undoubtedly are.

Equally, there is no name for the independence, courage, inner strength and special skills that are needed to make a life or to develop different episodes of life as a woman alone.

Every day the wine bars of the City are full of men giving each other (with somebody else's money) expensive food and drink to celebrate deals which they, clever old things, have just managed to pull off with only the help of someone to answer their telephone, someone to type their letters, squads of people to stroke their egos, someone to pay for their cars, someone to look after their children, someone to cook their dinners and iron their shirts and cheer them up when they're miserable. Pretty impressive.

I hope the 1990s will be a decade full of women naming the names of and taking the credit for the things they achieve, manage, invent, sustain, and generate. I hope we can learn to celebrate these things in ourselves and in each other.

Make a list of what you have achieved in the last two or five, or ten years (whichever you prefer). Name the hard times you have weathered, the risks you have taken, the people you have supported and helped, the machinery you have learned to operate, the strengths you have found in your own body, the projects you have undertaken and done.

Have you passed academic or professonal exams? Nursed

or supported relatives or friends through illness or depression? Perhaps you have coordinated your children's education or child care, or maybe you went on holiday alone for the first time? Learning to drive, joining a club, applying for promotion (whether you got the job or not), sorting out a long-term quarrel, are all achievements you may have accomplished without giving yourself credit, as too are keeping yourself healthy and your surroundings pleasant, growing flowers and vegetables, cooking food, and maintaining friendships.

Really begin to feel a calm pride in each item. Feel the pride and self-respect begin to ground and stabilize you.

Exercise 3: Noticing the cherry blossom

This is a very moving exercise. If you do not like, or feel too fragile at the moment to feel strong emotions on your own, do the exercise in the company of a friend you trust. We saw the blue/green planet earth for the first time from the 1969 Apollo moonshot. Watching the shots replayed twenty years later one heard a kind of quiet and reverence come over both crew and ground control when the earth in its place in the heavens swam into view. They stopped, momentarily, yattering about checking the retro whatsits and boosting the megathings. They soon resumed all that but every time there was an opportunity, kept angling the cameras back for another shot of the quiet innocent earth.

Our lovely planet which gives us life is desperately assailed. The grief and panic women and men are able to feel about it may generate enough energy to save it in time, or it may not, but mixed with our sense of our own ageing and death, our own limited time to experience the world, is the dreadful despair that the planet itself may be dying. We can make adjustments to how we use paper and petrol, we can vote Green and join Greenpeace, but mostly all we can do is bear witness, and not allow ourselves to be lied to.

The purpose of this exercise is to reaffirm what we love about the natural world, and renew our contact with it. Are there plants, or flowers, animals, birds, rocks, trees, waterways, cloud formations, or crystals, shells, any part of the natural world that you feel a particular affinity with? If there are thousands of things, choose one or two for now, and come back to some of the others some other time.

Talk, read, write, draw about the aspect of the natural world that you particularly love. Think of the times in the past when you have been able to be close to it, and of the times when you will again in the future. If it is a cyclical or seasonal thing, think how many of those seasons or cycles you have enjoyed and how many more there may be.

Although there is a sadness involved in noticing how finite our contact with the earth is, there is also an increase in our ability to value it.

2
Role Models

Where can we look for rôle models – women of age whom we would like to emulate, to gain strength from their ability to go ahead of us into the territory, to learn from their experience, their methods, their attempts and solutions, how to negotiate the time ahead?

The women used by the graphic design industry, the women used by the advertising industry, the women used by (most of) the film industry, are not helpful rôle models for ageing, because they're all young. A male newsreader gains in authority as his smile-lines deepen and his hair disappears or greys. Not so his sister newsreader who has to either be young or be so miraculously preserved and presented that one is astonished to find her to be over forty. (Not that there is anything wrong with looking youthful in itself, it's the way that it is used to exclude people who don't that is so negative.) She also, usually, has to be pretty and slim. I am looking forward to seeing large women reading the news, or disabled women reading the news, or women with peculiar dresses and bad haircuts (just as some of the men have odd ties and horrible haircuts) reading the news, because then we really will be looking at and taking seriously someone who is good at doing the job, and being decorative will clearly *not* be part of the job.

For a horrifying fable of a time where older women are becoming less and less in evidence (it turns out they are being 'used up' cleaning up radioactive debris) and all women are assigned fixed rôles, read Margaret Atwood's novel *The Handmaid's Tale*. (Not a book to read with a gun in your hand, it makes you so angry you would certainly shoot someone – but the anger it generates can be used for firing up positive power and energy.)

The only older women tolerated by the media seem to be those who completely deny their age and, presumably at huge expense of effort and money, look like women in their twenties. I find these women unhelpful as rôle models because in my view they set an agenda where the only valuable woman is young, thin and pretty, and where age has to be fled from and denied with a ghoulish intensity (however, see Jane's comments, page 24 below).

Most of us, of course, know or have experience of older women in our lives who do give us inspiration and clues as to how to live the second halves of our lives, and also we can begin collecting heartening and intriguing and inspiring images for women of age, and taking care to notice when an older woman does appear on the news or in the papers, looking, sounding, and being her age in a positive manner, and counting for something in the world. The people we choose will obviously be particular to us, we will not all choose the same kind of people. Variations will be to do with our political stance, our religious or philosophical points of view, our interest in or aversion to sport, fashion, the arts, the business world, and the general spectrum of our occupations and preoccupations. There will probably be some in our family or circle of friends and colleagues. We will notice some in public life. We may sometimes see a photograph or a drawing or a sculpture that gives a positive image of a woman in middle or old age, and has a positive message for us. We may read of women in fiction, or autobiographies which give us clues and ideas, or watch women in soap operas, who give us further data. A useful rôle model is not one who dazzles you so much that you feel inadequate: it is more a person whose qualities you admire, and can feel a tiny echo of in yourself. Such a person helps you to believe that you can develop and grow in those positive ways yourself. Maureen says:

> I watch older women. In pubs, on trains, walking around the place, I look and ask myself 'how do I want to be when

I'm older': and it's quite rare to see someone you can immediately say of, 'yes, I'd like to be like her'.

One of the first middle-aged women whom I admired is a sculptor. She was in her early forties while I was in my mid-twenties, at a time when the youth cult was at its height and gamine androgyny all the rage, and therefore a particularly anxiety-provoking era for middle-aged women. I was still assuming that the universe was a kind of movie in which I was the star, and therefore had the impression that not only would I never die, but also I would never be a middle-aged or old woman. However, I remember thinking that in the unlikely event of my ever actually ceasing to be an ingenue, I would like to be like this woman. What were the qualities in her that seemed to make being forty a pleasant, dignified, interesting state of affairs? She looked physically mobile, supple, and unselfconscious. I don't think she did 'exercises' or went on 'diets', but she had a lightness and grace, although I have no real impression of what her weight or her silhouette might have been like. She did not use make-up and her face was quite lined, her hands were battered and stained from working, and also strong and flexible. Her nails were chipped and flaky. Her hair was curly and long, and black with grey steaks in it. She was very sexy in a direct way but not flirtatious or tense or anxious about her body and her appearance. I would still like to be like her, although that would not necessarily be what everyone wants – the question is of course, how on earth did she do it?

I think a number of things played a part, looking at her from the outside. First, she had survived a great deal, and brought children up without a partner much of the time. The shapes, forms, and volumes of her own body may have given her just as much delight as the shapes, forms and curves of everything else which she studied in her work, so of course she was relatively free of the narrow stereotypes of loveliness of shape which most of us carry around, having instead a highly developed and personal insight. I suspect also that being satisfied and 'filled' by her work made her unlikely to become heavy by eating because she felt 'empty', and gave her an aspect of 'lightness' because of her professional perceptions and skills.

Perhaps in retrospect I am idealizing her, and doubtless I am oversimplifying her acceptance of herself and her ease in the world, but the picture of strength, self-respect, and sensuality is one that remains and sustains me as I try to find my own way.

Many women mentioned a physical assurance, and an ability to find and sustain true outside interests (different from, though undoubtedly often springing from, dilettante interests), as central to *their* positive rôle models, although the 'flavour' of those elements varies from woman to woman.

Joan admires a senior colleague who lives alone and impresses her with both her elegance and her outgoing social and travel diaries. She says:

> Daphne has great flair. Once or twice a week she works at home, but I know she will be sitting in front of her computer in beautifully coordinated clothes of lovely styles and colours, whether anybody else is going to see her or not. She is incredibly intelligent and successful, and does not suffer fools gladly: in fact I used to be frightened of her, but having known her for a long time I'm not any more. She's taken up spinning, weaving, and lacemaking, and she travels extensively, she has a very rich and full life. There is an eccentricity or idiosyncrasy about her too – I think that slight oddness adds to her vibrancy.

Catherine (seventy) had careers in teaching and property broking, and talks about her rôle model:

> An old Jewish lady I knew in the United States was an amazing example. She had been on the run all through the

> war. Her husband was sent to a concentration camp and died. Her children were sent to cousins in France and lived through it. She was so splendid, she lived through it all and never gave up. She was unable to trace her children until a year and a half after the end of the war. When I knew her she was in her eighties and racked with arthritic pain, and had lived through all that tragedy, but she was so lively, continued to go to theatre and operas, and did not let age or suffering defeat her, she never thought of herself as or behaved like a victim.

Her other rôle model surprises her: 'I've come to admire a woman whose work I used to dislike intensely, and that's Germaine Greer. I admire her integrity now.'

Susan (fifty-four, therapist) knows several contrasting women of age who inspire her.

> The first is an American woman who I met when she had just retired from a successful business career and was spending some time island-hopping in the Aegean. She is lean, tall, and outward-looking, ready for new ideas, but she has a strong fibrous stability.
>
> She made a point to me about how women stand – that once our breasts start to soften we tend to collapse our chests and bring our shoulders round as if to protect ourselves – how different you feel if you lift and open your chest and feel calm about your softening breasts.
>
> The second is a woman in her late sixties, a very respectable, established women, who is gentle and beautiful in what is, to me, a new way. She has a lover: this gives me a model of a new way of being sexual further into your life.
>
> The third woman is in her seventies, a peace activist, very poor financially: she has an amazing toughness, and humour and groundedness to do with her age.

As we shall see, an edge of eccentricity is often present in women who other women perceive as ageing in an admirable and interesting way.

Sometimes women completely outside of our cultural norms for acceptable appearance provide an example. It's easy to romanticize tribal and primitive lifestyles from our position of bourgeois angst, but with that proviso in mind many women found something to hold onto in the frank ageing of women in other communities. Joan's other positive image apart from the elegant Daphne is:

> . . . a woman I didn't know well – an old lady in a village where I have stayed in France, physically grotesque in a way, but in another way very fine. She's tough and independent, she's up at dawn feeding chickens and she's working all day. She's weatherbeaten and lined and she has only two teeth. She's full of activity and energy.

That energy and humour is something Hazel remembers in older African women she met while living in Africa for five years.

> They had such humour, they were so aware of the nonsense, the farcical side of life while living in what for us would be incredibly deprived circumstances. The 'deprived' situation cut so much rubbish out of life, it was down to the bare bones. There was great kindness and sharing, and these women were somehow completely themselves, completely uncompromised.

She also talks about 'an old French woman who had been part of a travelling circus – she lived in a railway carriage at the end of her son's garden: she had such a strong face. She had lived through appallingly hard times' – an ability to feel pain but still to survive – not to survive by shutting out the pain, but to survive through *feeling* it, is this why women so often admire women who have had a hard time but do not have a 'victim' mentality?

Hazel is also aware of women whose 'spirit' does not get confused by the structure of the rôles she lives out. Like the 'completely uncompromised' African women, Hazel also admires:

> . . . my best friend's mother. She has been a mother and a soldier's wife, both quite constricting rôles, but it hasn't diminished her as a human spirit. She has enormous warmth and all her caring is not self-sacrificing in tone, it's genuinely generous.

Christina (thirty-two, computer analyst) says she is encouraged by women in the second halves of their lives who 'continue to explore and develop themselves'. In fact, she describes:

> . . . not an individual, but a type I see in my mind – I see in ageing a potential for developing a better balance – being a person developed intellectually and in your career, and whose words have weight because of a wealth of experience. A woman ageing well needs to have a good sense of humour, an ability to break out of rôles, and a liking for the simple things in life.

However, having said 'I don't have any particular individual in mind', Christina remembers: 'My mother! My mother learned to swim when she was fifty-two, when she was *terrified* of water, and now she wants to learn scuba diving!' She goes on:

> I want to lose my fears. The younger you are, the more fears you have. I want to be someone who is fulfilled, who no longer has things to prove, and I'd like to confront my fears and get through them.

Jane also has a sense of an open mind and an open intellect being important faculties in the older women who she admires. She says:

> I hate it when people let their opinions get fixed, a sort of hardening of the intellectual arteries, when they won't really engage in dialogue any more but close discussions with things like 'well that's just the way I think'. So I admire older women who continue to think and evolve views and opinions: and both my nextdoor neighbours provide me with examples of women in their sixties who are like that. . . . In fact I am guilty myself of shutting things out in a middle-aged way when I can't cope with them – some of the dreadful things in the world I find I can't bear so I ignore them. For instance, women with babies begging in the subways is too much for me. I just don't want to know, so I suppose I close my mind in just the way I was saying I don't want to.

Jane does not share my reaction to unscathed film stars in their fifties:

> I think women like Joan Collins and Jane Fonda are good rôle models, they have successfully challenged what women in their forties and fifties can and are supposed to look like, and they have held onto their sexuality in a very positive way which age hasn't diminished at all.

Let us now praise famous women. Thankfully the activities of women's presses and women working in features, films and news coverage have given us much more access to the work, writing, experience, and activities of women than our mother's generation had. It's easier to find out about women artists, women medics, women mechanics, women war photographers, women aviators, women in every field than it used to be. We can also observe the growing (slowly, but still) number of women influential in public life. The heroines in public life admired by the women interviewed included:

Mother Theresa	Maya Angelou
Simone de Beauvoir	Joan Collins
Wendy Savage	The Queen Mother
Dora Russell	Catherine Cookson
Peggy Ashcroft	Mary Wesley
Freya Stark	Sybil Thorndike
Germaine Greer	Joanna Macey

Books by many of these women about themselves and their lives are listed in *Further Reading*, page 108.

The reiteration of being able to 'be more than' or 'break out of' rôles being an important requisite for rôle models in the private sphere is interesting, because the qualities mentioned as admirable among 'public' heroines included a stronge sense of admiration for anyone who had the strength to be some kind of an outsider, to challenge conventions and act independently when necessary, to follow personal conscience and conviction even if it meant stepping outside current rules and practice. Millament in Congreve's *The Way of the World* says with an ironic aristocratic drawl: 'I may, by degrees, *dwindle* into a wife'.

It's the refusal to dwindle into passive, invisible, and quiet middle and old age that distinguishes these women, and also an ability to choose personal belief and commitment over convention.

Look for powerful images of strong and/or ageing women in the world of art. Although many of the representations of women in painting, sculpture and photography may be of a voyeuristic kind which display and exploit young female beauty in a way which we find the antithesis of true celebration, there are images, if you look for them, of women whose femaleness and integrity with age may be inspiring.

There is a figure of a woman carved in limestone, between

27,000 and 30,000 years ago, about 4½ inches high, that was found in Willendorf in Austria. You can find her picture in most books on art history since she is regarded as the earliest representation of a human figure that has been found. Some women will find her heavy curves comic or offensive as clearly representing a preoccupation with fertility, but she is an ancient image whom I find powerful as a link with women through millennia experiencing life in a female body just as I do, and representing the heaviness, the curves, the processes of fertility.

In some ways Barbara Hepworth's sculptures make these same qualities in an abstract form – the hollowed spheres and ovals, sometimes strung with wires or strings, make a strong and non-ageist image of femaleness (that, again, is a personal interpretation of mine, you might feel quite differently about it).

Look out for the work of women photographers like Jo Spence and Grace Robinson to see images of strong, vivid, and real women at all stages of their lives, and notice the amazing beauty in direct and unmasked ageing women's faces.

Sometimes photographs of women from other cultures may move us. Women in nomadic tribes whose lives have been lived much more out of doors than most of ours have dramatic wrinkles.

Susan (fifty-four, therapist) feels a strong affinity for photographs:

> . . . of very old women with extremely wrinkled faces which are markers of their age. I'm always affronted by advertisements which say 'banish those telltale wrinkles' because I feel *I have a tale to tell*. I feel proud of women and their long, eventful lines. A face like that carries a lot of information. I'm proud of my own wrinkles, and sad that there are not more positive images of older women.

She also finds a character in so-called 'feminist science fiction' – those books which create other worlds in order to look at new ways of living, and also by the strangeness of contrast to see more clearly our present way of living – a help in making sense of her own ageing process:

> In Doris Lessing's *Marriages Between Zones 3, 4 and 5* there is a woman at the end who, although there's no clear indication of how old she is, goes into a zone away from people and into a strange personal place. It's austere, but also important and appealing.

Try these exercises in finding rôle models for moving on through new decades of your life. Use the resources of co-counselling, writing, and drawing as described in Chapter 1. Notice any dreams which come along around the time you are concentrating on any of these issues.

Exercise 4: Mirror, mirror (part 1)

(See Chapter 3 for Mirror, mirror, part 2, which also develops new ways of looking at ourselves.)

'Mirror, mirror, on the wall, who is the fairest of them all' – the old fairytale speaks out with the archetypal female anxiety, the older queen fears her place as the 'most beautiful' will be usurped by the younger princess. For a fascinating discussion of the subconscious and archetypal content of fairy tales, read Bruno Bettelheim's *The Uses of Enchantment*. However, this fear of younger women, and therefore anguish about our own ageing, is not there in the DNA, it is largely a social construct put upon us by all the things we have spoken of: the disregard of older women in our culture, the loss of power and identity associated with age. Social constructs cannot be shrugged off by a mere decision to do so, or by a wish to do so, but my impression is that they can sometimes be shifted enough to allow a bit more breathing space, and although they periodically crash back down onto you like a ten-tonne weight, one sometimes gets rid of them completely, for hours, days, weeks, even months at a stretch, with a feeling of glorious freedom.

Decide how to look in the mirror – are you going to look at your face in a small mirror, or a full-length mirror with your clothes on, or a full-length mirror with your clothes off? Do whichever you feel ready to do at the moment. Begin to shed your 'socialized' way of looking at yourself. Resist the urge to suck your abdomen in, or pinch away bits of flesh here and there, or to compose your face in any particular way. Lift up your spine, lift the crown of your head, release your shoulders back and down, breathe steadily and look at yourself, and begin to see what is happening to your face, your hair, your body, your limbs, your hands and feet (depending on how much of yourself you are looking at at the moment), as you pass through time. Maybe there are changes you feel angry or distressed about – have a look at Chapters 3, 5 and 6 if there are. However, see if there is at least one, maybe more, changes you can begin to celebrate. Sarah (thirty-seven, local government officer) says, 'I look in the mirror and I appreciate the lines on my face. They represent experiences in which I am proud of myself.'

Christina, thirty-two, says:

> I am enjoying my hands becoming tougher and more lined. I see how soft my children's hands are and remember when mine were like theirs, and my grandmother's and mother's hands were like mine are now: I am pleased to see the skilfulness and strength and use evident in my hands.

Maya (forty-six, administrator) says: 'If I look into my eyes I see a great depth of experience which I'm sure was not there when I was a younger women.'

Eve (forty-three) is pleased to see her feet:

> Age has brought an improvement to my feet. About a year

ago I decided to wear shoes that were the same shape as my feet and whenever I could to wear no shoes at all, and I have watched my toes uncross, unclench, and spread out, and my feet get stronger and more prehensile. I'm delighted that I have chosen (not before time!) to wear shoes that are right for me instead of trying to be right for the shoes.

The aim of this exercise is not to make a whimsical denial of the effects of ageing on our faces and bodies, but to take clear notice of any changes – increased definition, character, strength, peace, poise and so on – that *are* positive.

If you do not see any aspects of your age that you do enjoy, there is no need to fake it. If it leaves you feeling very negative, do two things – turn quickly to Chapter 3 to see some positive things you *can* do for your body, and come back to this exercise in a few weeks or months and do it again – you may find more to enjoy at another time, in another phase and another mood.

Exercise 5

You are the only you there ever has been, or could be. Nobody else can ever be you, or speak, move, love, hate, work, sleep, or dream, quite the way you do. Notice how often some kind of 'individual spirit' is mentioned among women as an important element in 'spirited ageing'. We all have that individual spirit, but for women in particular it often gets fogged over with a patina of fitting yourself into other people's lives. Caring for and supporting partners, parents, children, colleagues, may leave us unsure what our unique self is like. Try this guided fantasy to help you get in touch with your core self again.

If possible get a co-counselling partner to read this fantasy out to you slowly, pausing often, after you have made yourself comfortable lying on the floor. If you are working alone, read the fantasy through to yourself several times until the train of thought is clear to you. Lay down comfortably and let the fantasy drift through your mind.

Take a few deep breaths and sigh them away through your mouth, then let your breathing settle spontaneously – it will probably be slow and light. Feel your body, your head, your arms and legs – soft, heavy, and warm. Where you are in touch with the floor, sink into it a little more. Relax your feet, relax your hands. Let your face be smooth and soft.

Now take yourself in your imagination into a beautiful sunny garden. Notice what your garden is like, what plants and trees you see there. Walk slowly to your favourite place in the garden and lay down on a soft garden bed for a rest. Feel the sun soaking into you. Feel a soft breeze flickering over your body. Resting in your garden let your mind travel through your life, your experiences as a younger woman, as a little girl, as a baby. Take your time. Notice any times in your life when you felt particularly strong, particularly happy. Notice any times when you really felt happy in yourself. Notice any times at all that come to mind, however small the incident, however fleeting the moment. Hold those happy times gently in your mind.

Ask yourself if there is a word, or an image, or a colour, or any music, that expresses your quality as you are when you feel really at one with the world. If there is an image, a word, a colour, or any music, that seems to tell of you when you are most yourself, hold it gently in your mind.

When you are ready to do so, begin to wake yourself up. Do so by stretching your fingers, your toes, then yawning. Yawn some more and stretch your limbs and your spine. Curl up and roll over onto your side before you push your hands into the floor to help yourself to sit up.

If you feel subdued and quiet, spend a little time peacefully before you rush back into your day. If you want support ask your co-counselling partner to hold you for a while. If you are alone and feel sad, breathe steadily and have your sadness, it is only our stupid brash consumer culture that tells us you are only functioning properly when smiling and laughing. Most photographic images of women in magazines and on billboards are smiling, laughing and frolicking, as are the images of women projected as 'positive' in most TV advertising. Take with you into your life the insight into when you have felt 'most yourself', and any image or symbol you found for yourself. Look out for jewellery, postcards, poetry, images or sounds anywhere that have your symbol in them – you may like to have some of them around you.

Exercise 6: A decision

This exercise is a practical one, and involves you making one decision, however small, or however large, to find that 'transcendent interest' that is so lifegiving and energy-giving, mentioned by women as often present in the lives of women ageing well. Decide to make a start on something you want to do, and decide to make it a higher priority than all the things that flood into your mind as things you ought to do first (redecorate the kitchen, sew nametags into your children's clothes, take the worries off your husband's shoulders, clear up the backlog at work). It is your commitment to, or if you like your investment in, yourself.

You may not find what you really want straight away. If what you decide to study or the new skill or sport or language you learn doesn't in fact excite you, don't be afraid to try something else. Don't write yourself off as shallow. You have probably had little time in your life to be really in touch with what you as an individual want.

Follow any hunches and don't be put off if the activity you have a yen for is not trendy or right-on: stay with that spark in you that wants to follow something up, it will be right.

Make your decision public – tell a friend what you aim to do and when, ask for her support and encouragement, and ask her to check with you for the next month or two that you are, in the case of your one interest, putting it above the job, the housework, and other people's claims on your time.

Exercise 7: Taking pictures

It is remarkable how in many families the camera, and thus the record-making of the family's events and travels, rest with the men. Any photographer is also an editor, choosing what the significant people, moments, and panoramas are to pluck out of time and catch in a photograph. Maybe women would choose entirely different moments and people, views and scenes, to capture. In thinking as hard as we have in this chapter about visual experience, it is worth considering whether you want a camera of your own, to record the passing of time as you see it, and the places and people who matter to you. As an experiment a simple camera is quite cheap (although sadly the processing is very expensive). If it becomes an important activity to you, you could get a more elaborate camera later. Many women have spoken of how exciting and liberating they find it to be their own historians.

I have not done this yet and see countries, children, parties, and seasons, stuck in our album, but not as I felt and remember them. I look forward to making my own records. I also have a theme in my mind that I would like to photograph, linked with the contents of this chapter. I am moved by the beauty of any and everybody's face when they are immersed in an activity which completely absorbs them. Sports people, scientists, artists, children, anyone who is totally concentrating, seems to me to be beautiful, and one day I would like to make a series of photographs about this. Perhaps you too have a strand of reality you would like to photograph. This exercise suggests that you do it.

3
Body Fitness

In this chapter we consider how exercise may help us to be more loving towards ourselves and to enjoy the body we are living in as we move into the later phases of our age. Questions of skin care and diet are discussed in Chapter 5; here we will concentrate on movement.

> 'Stay young and beautiful
> It's your duty to be beautiful
> Stay young and beautiful
> If you want to be loved.'

This popular song of the 1930s gives us, in words scarcely credible in their crudeness in the 1990s, the reason why so many women bash away at various forms of exercise even when they hate it, even when they're tired, even when they're not 'getting results'. I wish I could say my moral and philosophical education came from Plato's *Republic* and light discussion of Rousseau round the family dinner table, but it didn't, it came from the lyrics of songs on the Light Programme and from the problem pages of *Woman* and *Woman's Own*, which in those days told women whose husbands strayed that they probably weren't making the home a welcoming enough place or themselves vivacious and attractive enough partners. I'm sure thousands of other women, like me, internalized all that responsibility and guilt: even though, like Maureen (see page 7), our intellectual and political thinking since has led us away from that view, there are still threads of it running through our attitudes and our decisions. When the old conditioning – 'it's all my fault', reappears, notice it, and try to reframe the thought in an assertive way: 'I notice such and such a problem, and want to be careful to make choices about improving this problem which suit me, and to take care to discuss the problem frankly with anybody else who has a responsibility involved in it.'

What I want to suggest here is the possibility of using movement, exercise, for other purposes than the direct one of 'staying young and beautiful', although if in the end that remains what any particular woman wants, I applaud and support her choice of what is right for her.

Consider this point: if you use exercise solely to fend off age, you will fail, because none of us can actually *stop* the ageing process. You *can* do several positive things for yourself – continuing with exercise will keep up the bulk of muscle and bone and help counteract the tendency of both to waste slightly as we age. Keeping joints loose and supple and spine stretched and flexed will make your movements loose, expansive, and expressive, and your body will speak for itself of confidence and self-respect. You will think of yourself as a person who *can* do things, not as a person who *cannot* do things. You will counteract anxiety by dispensing excess adrenaline while you exercise, and generating more of the hormones associated with peaceful or happy feelings – oxytocin, serotonin, and endorphins. All those things can be achieved by exercise and in themselves make you beautiful – but I doubt that exercise pursued *solely* in order to be beautiful has quite the same results. All those things will slow down or transform the kind of changes to our bodies we know are to do with age; but again, if you exercise with the narrow purpose of delaying age, I doubt the results are as striking as the strength and grace evident in women who love this or that exercise for its own sake.

The suggestion here is to think about shedding negative reasons for exercise (I'm afraid of getting fat, I'm afraid of getting frumpy, I'm afraid of looking stiff and creaky) and choosing an exercise for positive reasons – for opportunities of *finding* your whole self, rather than *losing* bits of yourself (weight, age, flab). This is not as esoteric as it sounds – just think of anyone you know who *has* found a physical form of discipline with which she is at home, and notice the fluidity and radiance that emanates from such a person. Once you become aware of this element in choosing a type of exercise, age or fear of approaching age makes very much less difference in having courage to try it or worrying about what you'd look like if you do. Hans Joachim Stein, in his book *Kyudo: The Art of Zen Archery*, points out how age and experience is seen as of great value in this Eastern discipline, in contrast with the end-gain performance sports of the West:

> Western sport . . . is usually concerned with record performances or at least high achievements, which are for the most part only possible up to the age of forty. A price has to be paid for the one-sided emphasis on the body and technique. . . . Such an 'age-limit' is completely alien to Kyudo. In fact, the older and more mature the archer, the more profound his penetration of the Way of the Bow is likely to be. The best archers, technically and spiritually, are usually the older masters.

Distressingly sexist in its language (what about women *Kyudoka*? why on earth use the word 'penetrate' to mean 'understand'?), though this may be the fault of the translation, it is nevertheless clear that this view of *Kyudo* can illuminate our thinking about movement and age.

How does one begin to look for a system or style of exercise where one will feel 'at home' and able to 'find oneself'. Some are activities that you can begin by yourself informally, or with a friend, with minimal equipment and organization. Some are techniques or skills that you will want to learn in a class. Most sports and dance centres and most local authority adult education sections offer a bewildering array of classes. Take your time choosing a class that is right for you; much depends on finding an empathetic and inspiring teacher. Ask if you can observe a class before you join it, and if you have any doubts about the attitude of the teacher and the atmosphere, don't go. It is sad to know that women who have gathered up the courage to go to a physical class, and are not received and taught carefully and well, will probably go home (a) with a great sense of personal failure, and (b) not be willing to try again for months or even years. Be confident if you *don't* like a class. You have the right to choose the style, the atmosphere, and the teacher you like and to trust your own judgement in this matter.

Walking

'I've just been on a women's walking holiday and walked 200 miles with nine other women. It was glorious! When I walk long distances I feel so free, I feel fit and healthy, I'm not oppressing anyone; I feel I could walk forever.' Maureen did indeed glow with health and satisfaction describing her recent trip.

Susan felt in touch once again with the land in the summer, having been shut in various offices all year:

> I had forgotten how much I love the chalk lands. With a friend I had a long walk through the Wye valley – the flowers we saw, so many species, and the butterflies: and then we saw a sort of parade of British mammals: it became almost funny how they appeared one after another – a deer, a weasel, a fox, a stoat. I was so moved. We also walked some of the way on Roman roads and I could feel the echoes of the past on those roads, the thousands of people moving along them, hundreds of years ago.

There are many clubs, societies, and organized holidays available for 'serious' walking, equipment for which includes boots and waterproofs. Less 'serious' walking, of course, may be taken up more informally. For women, sadly, the issue of safety is always with us, and walking and exploring alone is a risk many of us no longer feel able to take, although some women decide to do so and take great delight in their lone journeys. It has to be an individual decision for each woman. If you do decide to walk alone, consider leaving information with at least one person about where you are going and when you expect to arrive at the next stage of your travels, so that someone is quickly aware if you do go missing.

Dervla Murphy is a woman who has chosen to walk alone far and wide over the continents of the earth. Her many books transport those of us who doubt our shoes will carry us that far, to the Indus Valley, to sunrise in the Andes, and many other distant panoramas. These travel books, and the books and journals of other women explorers and travellers, can give an imaginative experience of wider spheres during parts of our life when we are confined by necessity to a narrow range of places.

Susan finds the absolute sense of the earth beneath her feet very moving: 'I look forward to walking the terrain in this country and other countries. I would like to see that going on into my very oldest age.'

Running

As well as walking, Maureen runs:

> I like to go jogging, it's easy to organize, and I feel it's proper exercise. When I go for a run I feel proud. My mother couldn't have done it at my age. It's not her fault, I loved her and admired her, but she never did anything for herself.

Many women get enormous pleasure and a sense of strength and self-reliance from their running, especially when after a few weeks or months their fitness and flexibility increases and they suddenly feel their legs stretch and stride out as they run.

Safety is again a consideration and joining a women's or

mixed running group should ensure that there is always company with which to run. There is no need to run competitively if you don't want to, but many women enjoy the personal challenge of building their own strength, endurance and speeds. The London marathon provides a yearly inspiration, and undermined though sport may be at the moment by financial and drug scandals, few of us watch the finish of this huge race without a lump in the throat. Elizabeth said 'I was so moved when I saw the London marathon on TV this weekend that I made a commitment to myself that next year I would be there too. I began to find out how to prepare myself.'

Since only one man and only one woman can 'win' the London or any other marathon, everybody else is really running as part of their own process of inner growth, and who knows what fears are confronted, what pride, sorrow, pain, failure, and success are faced by each individual each time the race is run.

One more word about marathons. One participant made a comment which I feel has a peculiar resonance with women's lives. 'The twenty-six miles are easy,' he said, 'it's the 385 yards that are difficult.' How many times have you weathered a twenty-six mile day only to find that at the eleventh hour some new contingency means you have to push through another 385 yards? No wonder women are good at running marathons.

For advice on equipment, warm-ups, preliminary training and starting to run, look at *Women Running* by Liz Sloan and Ann Kramer.

Cycling

As a cheap and independent way of moving around cycling gives many women a sense of great exhilaration:

> It's my way of moving around the world in a very free, fresh, and poised way, I like the harmoniousness that

> cycling has. It isn't brash, it isn't harming the world, it feels as natural as birds flying. I also like the fact that it means I have to cut down on how much stuff I carry around.
>
> I like cycling, I do it on purpose to stay fit, and I like the fact that it isn't abusing the environment, it's quiet, discreet, and doesn't cause pollution. It gives me a feeling of independence.

If the area you have to cover most days is fairly small, you might want to consider making cycling your main form of daily transport. If you have a choice of the type of bike, choose one which you can ride with your spine fairly upright, your chest open and your shoulders relaxed. You need good waterproofs for wet weather, and a luminous belt and sash or jerkin make you very much more visible, and therefore very much safer, if you ride in the dark. Your stamina and strength will improve through regular cycling.

Yoga

Christina says:

> Yoga is a continuing rock. It is always there to go back to. Once it has been part of your life it never goes away. It is always available to get any strength that's in you out when you need it.

And Alice comments:

> I did not start yoga to counteract age or anything. I did it for my own personal purposes and it's become an exploration of my being and therefore part of my ageing. It has increased my suppleness, helped me to find a permanent strength in myself, not through violent or vigorous action, I feel strong in stillness. Spirit, body, and mind, to me are all

one thing, undivided. Yoga is a focused way of addressing all of them. Yoga has helped me to *become* my body.

I began yoga twenty years ago, shortly after my first child was born. I was in somebody's room, and she said 'I'm going to yoga, do you want to come?' and I went. It's true to say I was never the same again. For one thing, I had always felt useless in gym, games, and dance. I was uncoordinated, and felt inadequate. Second, I was dimly aware that pregnancy and birth, gone through on an ill-informed diet and with no attempt at exercise at all (one didn't then) had had a devastating effect on my vulnerable teenage body. The class was in a garden, on a summer evening, redolent of roses. The teacher's voice was calm and sure. She said 'There's no competition, no prize. Do what's right for you for today.' I cannot describe what it meant for what I did to be enough, respectable, beautiful in itself. I'm sure to anybody who doesn't do yoga, this sounds gushing, but it is, if anything, an understatement of the wonderful resource that yoga is. You start from where you are, you work in your own time and at your own pace. Flexibility, strength and moments, at least, of serenity, come. An acceptance of and a deep love for one's own body in all its many states (fat, thin, tired, energetic, tense, erotic, sleepy, restless) begins to awaken, and through that a deep love for other people's bodies. You need loose clothing, a clean, clear space, and a bit of time, to begin yoga. You could begin by yourself using one of the many books available such as *The Book of Yoga* (Sivananda Yoga Group) or *Stretch and Relax* (M. Tobins and M. Stuart), or by attending a class. If you go to class, trust your own feelings about the atmosphere of the class and the attitude of the teacher. The class should have a calm atmosphere of mutual respect and helpfulness, the teacher should be gentle, without a strident ego, well-qualified and informed. If the first class you try doesn't feel right for you, have the courage of your convictions and move on to another. Enjoy the journey into your self and outwards into a new relationship with the world.

Martial arts

After some years studying yoga I became interested in the martial arts, with some instinct that martial arts and yoga are the different sides of the same coin. The kicks and strikes of the martial arts are like the sudden explosion or flowering out of yoga poses. The philosophy, far from being violent, is absolutely peaceful. The more martial arts skill one has, the less violence one draws towards oneself, because one becomes more calm and centred.

The philosophical basis of the two disciplines is the same, an inclusive system that accepts and balances the darkness and the light, the hard and the soft, the swift and the slow, the heavy and the light, all possible opposites.

Tae Kwon Do

My own particular love is *Tae Kwon Do*, the Korean 'hard' style. In the study of *Tae Kwon Do* I have learned about courage, endurance, perseverance, vulnerability, about help and respect for one another, about conflict fair and foul. I have discovered abilities and strengths in my body beyond all my expectations, and glimpses, in my messy, unbeautiful life, of pure Zen. I would urge women in the second halves of their lives not to be afraid to learn a 'hard' style martial art. A good class, again, has a calm atmosphere of interdependence and help, and a well-qualified, well-informed teacher who is without any arrogance. The emphasis is on personal progress, not athletic performance. Your honest best is expected of you but no more. You will sweat hard, but stop short of injury. Observe or try a class to ensure that it is a place you feel you will be able to look after your body well. Notice whether there are women among the senior grades in the class; if not, perhaps the women in the class are not really supported and encouraged, and perhaps you would prefer to spend your time elsewhere.

T'ai ch'i

Many women are drawn to the 'soft' styles, particularly *t'ai ch'i*, an ancient Chinese exercise system rooted in Taoist philosophy, whose origins stretch back at least 4000 years. *T'ai ch'i* is essentially a flowing succession of movements, which are beautiful to watch and to perform. The slowness with which the movements are performed allows the practitioner to become sensitive to the subtleties of the movement, and to sense the harmonizing of those subtleties with the rhythms of the world around. Select a class you like, with the same provisos as for yoga and 'hard' martial arts classes. Equipment is not expensive, and again there is the advantage of taking part in an activity where personal growth and mutual help are the aim, not competition.

Dancing

Mary trained with the London Contemporary Dance Theatre. She knows that dance can be a way back into inhabiting your body fully. She says:

> Creative dance as I see it is to do with developing the physical, mental, and spiritual aspects of a person. It is not to do with imposing a technique *on* the body, it is to do with bringing out the dance that is already *in* the body. It is making a way for a person's vitality to come out. Technique does have some advantages, as for instance in contemporary dance, and these are to give a vocabulary of movements within which to express yourself, and also a measure of safety, in that with good posture and good technique one's spine and joints are protected. I feel there is a loss of spontaneous movement nevertheless.

Circle dance has made dance very accessible to people

who still consider that they can't dance. It's a way of dancing with a group of people and enjoying it without worrying about whether your feet are in the right place. People can often move onto more creative dance within the safety of doing that.

Mary's own work with dance has led her into the area of healing. She says:

Dance therapy might be the nearest way for adults to work with movement towards personal discovery. It is used in acute situations, but could be used to great effect more generally.

I do only a small amount of performing and no teaching in the conventional sense at the moment. The creative ideas still come to me, and they still work, but I am tired of putting my understanding and feelings about dance over in that way. I want to work in the healing sector, I'm interested in being aware of where the energy is within you and moving it to different parts of yourself. The most frustrating thing is just trying to make it generally accessible to large numbers of people. I would like to be facilitating as a counsellor so that individuals can come to understand the self through the body – finding fulfilment in ourselves as we are.

Mary's thoughts about circle dance and dance as healing may ring bells with you and you may want to find out what such an exploration could mean to you. Listings and information for classes and workshops in this field can be found in *New Dance Magazine*, which can be ordered from Dance Bookshop, Cecil Court, London WC2.

Jazz dancing, contemporary dancing, belly dancing, flamenco dancing, Sufi dancing, ballroom dancing, tap dancing, and many many more styles are taught at dance studios and local authority evening classes all over the country. If you are attracted by the idea of expressing yourself and having fun dancing, get syllabuses from local centres and studios. Follow your hunch as to what you feel like learning, and also trust your intuitive reaction to the teacher and to whether she or he is the right person for you to be learning with now. Mary has the same feeling about dancing as I do about drawing: 'Everyone can dance, all children dance naturally, but sadly most people begin to believe they can't during their adolescence, and continue to believe it right through their adult life. It isn't true though, everybody can.'

Everybody can. This means *you*!

'Anti-exercises'

Maybe you still feel uninspired to participate in any form of exercise. If so Thérèse Bertherat's beautiful book *The Body Has its Reasons* may open the door of your own physical experience to you. Bertherat is very much opposed to the punitive aspects of many modern western exercise régimes, and at the close of her book suggests some exploratory movements called 'preliminaries' which involve no 'effort' in the usual physical sense, but an effort of imagination and responsiveness instead.

Exercise 8: Routine magic: stretching for freedom

Here is a short set of stretches to begin to limber up your body. If you are fit and flexible these can be used to loosen up and wake up – a sort of all-over yawn. If you are feeling out of touch with your body, it is a gentle way to get in contact again. Wear loose clothes, and have a clean, clear space on the floor. Make all the movements slowly and gracefully. Do not force anything.

As Voyager 2 reached Neptune in 1989 we heard that the computer recoding linking the old computer on the spaceship with the new software on earth is known among programmers as 'routine magic': such a touching name. Stretching is the 'routine magic' of the body, linking the alienated body to the more aware one.

Sitting well Start by sitting crosslegged on the floor. If your knees are too stiff, try putting a cushion under either knee. If this is not comfortable, sit on a cushion and stretch your legs out in front of you, knees 18 inches apart. Make sure you are sitting right on your hip bones, not curved back onto your tail bone: this will give you a lifted, spacious feeling. Start to lift up out of your hips. Lift your abdomen lightly but don't press it back. Women have such trouble with their stomachs feeling that the only alternatives are to slop it forwards or to jam it back. There is a middle way, holding and lifting the stomach gently. With practice you will find it. Keep lifting up through the spine (feel your chest open and your shoulders relax back and down), up through the back of your neck, and feel the crown of your head lifting towards the ceiling.

Breathing Let your eyes close and start to breathe a little more deeply and a little more slowly than usual. Keep your spine lifting and your face relaxed. Place both hands on your abdomen below your navel. Do not get in a state about the shape and feeling of your abdomen. Relax. Accept this lovely round, soft, part of your body.

As your breathing settles into a rhythm, let your abdomen rise slightly into your hands as you breathe in, and collapse back from your hands as you breathe out. Your stomach expands as you breath in, collapses slightly as you breathe out. This helps you to breathe fully. If it is the opposite way round from your usual breathing (that is, you suck your stomach in as you breathe in, and release it as you breathe out) you have got into a habit of shallow breathing with only the upper part of your lungs. Continue practising deeper breathing and you will soon find yourself doing it all or most of the time. It is the same easy, innocent breathing you see in sleeping children or young animals.

Head and neck After a few minutes of breathing like this become aware of your posture again. If your spine has sagged, lift it up.

Take your hands gently away from your abdomen and link them behind your head. Drop your head forwards, chin onto your chest, let your forearms come down on either side of your face. Feel the stretch in your neck and upper shoulders. Keep your spine lifting, your shoulders releasing down, your abdomen lightly lifting. Breathing is steady. After a few steady breaths, float your head up to the centre on a breath in, and take your hands down onto your knees.

As you exhale, stretch your throat up, chin pointing to the ceiling, head falling back. Think of stretching your throat, not snapping your head back. After a few breaths, float your head up to the centre.

Exhaling, drop your right ear to your right shoulder. Hold for a few breaths, then inhale, come up, exhale, stretch your left ear to your left shoulder, inhale, come up to the centre.

Be aware of your posture. If your spine is sagging, lift it again.

Drop your chin onto your chest, then roll your head around in two very big, very slow circles. Take your own amount of time, and notice what you feel as you go. Then do two circles in the other direction, and come back to the centre again.

Shoulders Sit up out of your hips. Try pressing your hands palm to palm behind your back. If that is too difficult, hold opposite elbows, or hold opposite wrists behind your back. Keep your face soft and your breathing steady. Feel your chest and shoulders open. Hold for a few breaths then slowly release.

Still sitting on your buttock bones (ischial tuberosities is their official name!) not back to your tailbone (coccyx), and sitting tall with your legs crossed, relax your shoulders back and down. Wriggle your left hand up between your shoulder blades. Inhale, stretch your right elbow, reach down towards your left hand behind your back. If you can, clasp your hands together. Maybe your left hand seems miles away! If so, when you stretch your right hand up hold a scarf, or a legwarmer or sock in it, and it will hang down your back when you bend your right elbow, so you can catch it with your left hand.

Hold the stretch for a few breaths, then breathe in and stretch your right hand up towards the ceiling, exhale and stretch your arm out and down. Slide your left hand down.

Now do the whole thing on the other side. You may be amazed to find how asymmetrical you are. But with time, the two sides of your body will even up.

Gentle twist Sit up well out of your hips. Lengthen the back of your neck. Balance your head on top of your neck like a flower on a stalk. Put the back of your left hand on the right of your right knee. Breathe in, lift your spine. Exhale, twist, look over your right shoulder, put your right hand on the floor level with your spine. Feel a gentle twist. Keep your weight in your hips, do not drop it back onto your back hand. Hold for a few breaths, then inhale and come back to centre. Exhale and twist to the other side. Hold for a few breaths then inhale and come back to centre.

Standing stretches Stand with your feet hip distance apart. Tuck your tailbone in, grow tall up through your spine. Lift your abdomen lightly. Release your shoulders back and down. Lift the crown of your head up towards the ceiling, open and lift your chest. Relax your face, steady your breathing.

Become aware of your footprints on the ground, and make them even. Sense the soles of your feet rooting down through the floor, the concrete, down and down towards the earth. The crown of your head is stretching up, sensing, through the building, the sky above. Feel the balance and freedom of this stance.

Side stretch Step your feet 3–3½ feet apart. Turn your left foot in, right foot out. Keep your hips and chest facing the front. Breathe in and stretch your arms straight out to the sides at shoulder height. Exhale and release your shoulders, and stretch your fingertips even further. Breathe in again and stretch up out of your hips, exhale, and stretch out to the right and then down, placing the back of your right hand on the right leg on the knee, calf, or foot – however far down you can manage without tipping your body forwards. Your left arm stretches straight up in the air, palm of your hand facing the front. Hold the stretch for a few breaths, then breathe in and come up to the centre, exhale and float your arms down to your sides. Make the stretch to the other side, and hold for a similar number of breaths before coming back up to the centre again.

Warrior stretch Stand your feet wider apart (4–4½ feet). Turn your left foot in, right foot out. Keep your hips and chest open

Side stretch

Warrior stretch

to the front. Keep your spine vertical throughout the stretch, do not tilt to right or left. Keep your tailbone tucked under, your abdomen lifting lightly, the back of your neck long. Breathe in, lift your arms straight out to the sides, shoulder height, exhale, relax your shoulders and extend your fingertips even more. Breathe in again, and as you breathe out, bend your right knee until your calf is vertical, your thigh parallel to the floor. Do not shoot your knee out beyond your right foot. If you cannot come down so far, go to your own comfortable maximum for today. Keep your spine vertical, hips and chest face the front. Hold for a few breaths.

Breathe in, and come back up to the centre, exhale, float your arms down to your sides.

Do the same stretch to the left side, holding for a similar number of breaths.

Balance If you do not normally stand around on one leg, learn this balance holding onto something for support. You will soon find you can balance happily on one leg.

Use a heavy chair or the wall for support. Stand on the leg next to the support. Put your foot down and spread out your toes, feel you are making a big, broad footprint. Bend the other knee, turning it out to the side, and place the foot on the standing leg's ankle, knee or groin whichever is appropriate for you. Tuck your tailbone in and lift up through your spine. Lift the crown of your head. You are aiming eventually to turn the bent knee out into the same plane as your hips.

Now focus your gaze on something. It can be anything, a mark on the wall, a detail on a picture, whatever. When you get into the habit of stretching you can arrange something beautiful to look at when you balance – a flower, shell, stone, crystal, anything you enjoy gazing at.

If a balance comes, join your hands palm to palm in front of you. If it doesn't, don't worry. It will one day. Give it time.

Hold your balance for a few breaths, then step gently down. Do the balance on the other side, not forgetting to turn around if you are using support, and to stay in the balance for a similar number of breaths.

Wide stance forward stretch If you have recently slipped a disc or had a back injury omit this stretch. When you begin to recover, do the modified version, progressing as you improve to the full stretch. If in doubt when to begin this stretch, consult your general practitioner. If you have high blood pressure at the moment, do the modified stretch only.

Stand with your feet 4–4½ feet apart. Feet should be parallel, toes pointing forwards. Sense your footprints on the floor. Breathing in, imagine you are drawing the breath up through your legs, hips and chest. Stretch your arms straight up into the air and draw the breath up your arms and into your finger tips. Exhaling, stretch forwards, hinging at the tops of your thighs not the back of your waist. Lift your abdomen. When you cannot stretch any further forwards begin to release down. If you cannot get your hands on the floor, hold onto opposite elbows, and relax your head and neck. Do not bounce.

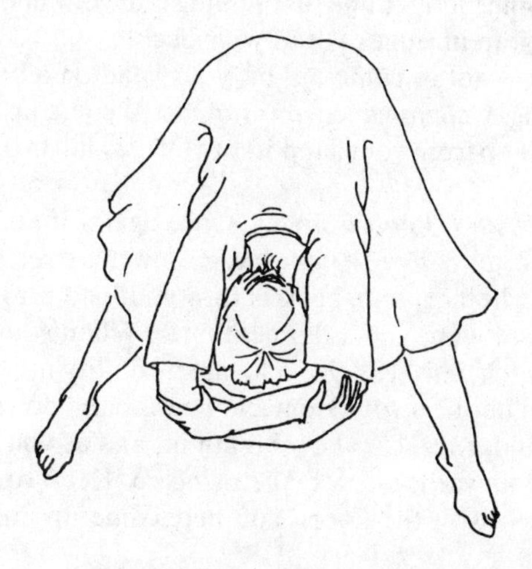

Wide stance forward stretch

If you can reach the floor, bring your hands back in line with your feet as far as you can, and relax your head and neck.

If you are very supple, bend your elbows, clasp your hands gently behind your head, and rest your head and elbows on the floor as close in line with your feet as you can.

Hold the stetch for a few breaths, then inhale and lift your head, exhale and walk your feet in towards each other until you feel safe to press your feet into the floor and come up.

Modified stretch Use a heavy table, or kitchen worktop, or desk, to support you in this modified stretch.

Stand facing this stable surface, 2 or 3 feet away (adjust your distance as you do the stretch). Step your feet 4–4½ feet apart, feet parallel, toes pointing forwards. Inhale and stretch up, exhale and stretch forwards, bending at the tops of your thighs, not the back of your waist. Hold onto the surface.

Walk your feet back (or forwards), until your legs are vertical (if you are not sure get a friend to adjust you in the stretch). Make your spine long, think of it sinking into your body rather than sticking up in ridges out of your back.

When you want to come up, lift your head on a breath in, and, exhaling, *walk towards your support* to come up. Do not fling yourself up from your support or you may hurt your back.

Floor stretches – (1) cobra stretch Once again, if you have a recent back injury or vulnerable back, omit this stretch. If you are unsure whether your back is in a good state to do this stretch, consult your general practitioner. When your back is ready to stretch, this will give a lovely flexibility.

Lie on the floor on your stomach, hands palm down on the floor at shoulder level. Take a breath in, and as you breathe out, unwind upwards like a snake rising up. Keep your pubic bone in touch with the floor. You may come up only a few

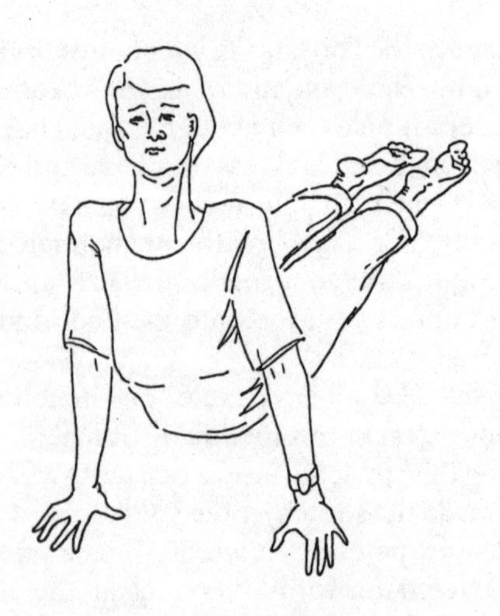

Cobra stretch

Cobbler stretch

inches or rise up vertically, or be somewhere in between. Do what is right for you. Hold for a few breaths, then flow forwards onto the floor again on a breath out, and rest your face to one side. Let your breathing and heartbeat return to normal. Sometimes when people learn this stretch their wrists and hands feel pitifully weak. Don't despair. With practice a strong feeling will eventually come.

Repeat the stretch again, and when you finish, go up onto all fours and then, exhaling, sit back on your heels and lie down (or begin to) along your thighs, arms and hands stretching out in front.

After a rest in this position inhale and lift your head, exhale and sit up.

Floor stretches – (2) cobbler stretch Indian cobblers sit this way. Sit up tall, make sure you are sitting on your hip bones, not your tail bone. Bring the soles of your feet together, and

Hero stretch

drop your knees out to the side. Move your feet as close to your perineum as you can, and hold them in your clasped hands. Open and lift your chest, don't squash it between your upper arms. Lift your abdomen gently. Close your eyes and breathe steadily. Little by little a wonderful flexibility will come and your knees will one day rest on the floor.

If you are tired, practise this stretch sitting up against the wall. If your knees feel very stiff, place one or two cushions under each knee.

Stay in the stretch for a few breaths. When you want to come out of it, let go of your feet, lift up your knees with your hands, and stretch your legs out in front.

Hero stretch If your knees are flexible, you can move straight into this position by kneeling up, separating your feet, and sitting down between them. If not, put one, two or more cushions between your feet, and then sit down. As your knees loosen up with practice you will be able to remove the cushions one by one, and eventually sit on the floor.

Link your hands, push them away from you, palms out, and then stretch your arms up, palms pushing up towards the ceiling. Try to feel the stretch coming up from your base on the floor, rather than from your armpits.

Hold the stretch for a few breaths, then exhaling, float your arms down, unclasp your hands, and then straighten out your legs.

Twist Sitting on the floor, stretch your right leg straight out in front of you, bend your left knee, and put the foot flat on the floor, close in to the perineum.

Put your left hand on the floor behind you and leaning gently back onto it turn to your left, putting the right of your armpit to the left of your left knee. Exhaling, straighten your spine up, turn and look over your left shoulder, and lift your

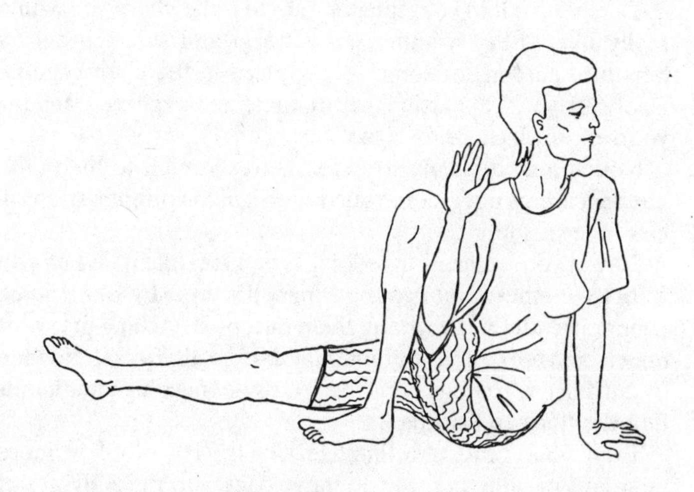

Twist

right palm to face outwards. Breathe steadily, and stay in the twist for a few breaths. When you finish, breathe in and come back to the centre, exhale and untangle yourself. Repeat, for a similar number of breaths, to the other side.

Relaxation

Finish your stretching with a few minutes' deep relaxation. Lie on your back on the floor. If your lower back feels tight, bend your knees up, feet flat on the floor. Turn your toes in slightly, and let your knees fall together. Feel your lower back release.

Close your eyes, and roll your head very, very slowly from side to side, until all tightness is gone from your neck and shoulders. Settle your head in the centre. Make sure your chin is not pointing up to the ceiling. If it is, lengthen the back of your neck, and gently draw your chin in. Let your arms and hands roll away from your sides until your shoulders feel open. Imagine all your muscles relaxing, all your joints loosening.

Take yourself in your imagination to somewhere you would really like to be, whether it's a warm and sunny beach, a beautiful garden, or some lovely place in the countryside – wherever you feel particularly at home and at peace – and lay yourself down there for a rest.

Notice how dynamic stretching gives stretch to the body, but relaxation puts us in touch with our own inner strength and inner resources.

Stay in your relaxation as long as you feel like it. When you want to re-emerge into your ordinary life do so by taking some deeper breaths and yawning them out, by stretching first your fingers and toes, then your limbs and spine, like a cat, and then by curling up, rolling over onto your side, pushing your hands into the floor and sitting up.

Take your time. Acclimatize slowly. Have a few more moments of quiet before you move back into the activities of your day.

Exercise 9: Mirror, mirror, part 2

Have a look at your whole body in a mirror. Decide whether to have lots, few, or no clothes on when you do this. If, like me, you have no full-length mirror, you will have to climb on and off chairs in order to see your whole self. Be careful when you do this! Perhaps there is some meaning in never having chosen to spend money on a mirror in which you can see your whole self. It is notoriously difficult for women to see themselves in mirrors properly. On holiday in a rented house I said completely disingenuously to a friend, 'There's something wrong with the mirror on the stairs. I look thin in it.' 'Listen to yourself,' he said.

Look at your whole body in your mirror and begin to try to observe it calmly and without panic. If any part of your body catches your attention think of all the positive things this part of your body has done. (For example, if it's your hands, think of all the work they've done, all the skills they have, all the things they've carried, all the people they've held.) Think of loving that part of your body. If hate or sadness arises, feel it and allow it, but notice that the feeling could change.

I have suffered all my (post-pubertal) life from a sense of woeful inadequacy about my breasts. I always felt that they were too small, and then they were badly stretchmarked by my first pregnancy, and then seemed too soft and shapeless after breastfeeding and so on – and I know hundreds of women feel the same about their breasts (or similar things about other parts of their body). But after hearing me moan about this finally a friend said: 'For heaven's sake, think about all the pleasure your breasts have given to so many people and how many children they have fed and comforted.' This helped me – I had never thought of that before. My feeling of inadequacy didn't disappear overnight and can still surface when I feel vulnerable, but it did begin to alter and I began to feel better. I also began to be aware of how much sensual pleasure *I* get from my breasts – when I started to feel better that pleasure was available in full flood. A few years after that comment from my friend I think my breasts actually *are* fuller and 'prettier', and anyway I *feel* very much better, most of the time.

So, look at your body, appreciate the experience, the capacities, of each part, and while not expecting sad feelings magically to disappear, emphasize what good feelings your can.

If when looking at yourself there are things you want to change that you could change (treating rough areas of skin with cream, beginning to exercise muscles that have become weak, making sure part of yourself gets into the sunshine sometimes), think about how, when, and where you would like to begin to make these changes.

4

The Menopause – What Sort of Change?

The menopause used to be colloquially called 'the change of life', and self-help books often pun in their titles on the 'no change' or 'change for the better' theme, while women may feel 'short-change' and 'a change for the worse' describe their uncomfortable symptoms more realistically.

As always, the dilemma for women is this: if we strive for equal status professionally, intellectually, politically, written into that initial struggle is a tendency to suppress awareness and manifestation of our physical female life-events (menstruation, pregnancy, menopause). They can be quoted too easily as (spurious) indicators of weakness, vacillation, unreliability. In fact we need to learn to see them ourselves and demonstrate them to others for what they really are: indicators of strength, endurance, and adaptability.

The trap on one side is to be argued into an inferior position because of supposed 'weakness', but on the other to take on a great weight of denial, suppression, and isolation, pretending under pressure that the physical aspect of our femaleness doesn't exist.

Our aim might be to try to acknowledge, celebrate, and evaluate our experiences for ourselves, and decide how much or how little to let them impact on our schedules and our lives.

Certainly for many women, the 'climacteric', the time surrounding the 'menopause' (the final menstrual period, which of course you only know in retrospect was the last period), is a time of upheaval and reappraisal, accompanied by definite physical symptoms. This is not to say that 'menopausal' women should be written off, thought of as incapable of professional responsibility and personal coherence. (It is interesting how the very word 'menopausal' has come to have an insulting connotation, like 'hysterical' and so many of the words associated with women's bodies, and it might be useful to women to find another word to denote this part of their lives.) Nor should the importance and impact of this time be ignored. The balancing act is a delicate one, but then balancing is a skill most women have developed to an advanced level, and are well able to manage.

The ending of fertility is a milestone, however much of a burden or a mixed blessing that fertility has been. Some women are overjoyed to be shot of the whole apparatus of contraception once and for all. (If you begin the menopause under fifty years of age you should continue with contraception for two years following your last menstruation. If you begin the menopause over fifty, you should continue with contraception for one year after your last period.) Others, while clear in their minds that a baby is the last thing they want or need, still feel a sadness that the fertility is gone.

Hazel's youngest child was born when she was thirty-nine. She was sterilized by tubal ligation shortly afterwards and was quite clear that she did not want more children. Even so she says: 'When I went through the menopause I had to grieve over losing the ability to create life. I knew that there now was no way I could ever manage it again. A biological chapter was over.'

For Susan, although she had dreaded this, it did not hurt in the way she had expected: 'I was quite frightened about losing my fruitfulness and femaleness, and in fact I don't feel any loss.' Susan was surprised because she had expected the experience of the climacteric to dominate her life for at least a number of months. In fact, she says:

> I expected the menopause to define me in some new way, and because it hasn't I'm left having to define myself. I thought it would turn me into a certain kind of person, but it was simply a rather slight physical experience. I am freer, but I am having to define for myself where I am.

Women who have not had children even though they longed for them, may find themselves faced again with the vividness of that pain, when the periods finally stop and the last dream of fertility has gone. Even women who chose not to have children are sometimes surprised to feel a pang when the possibility is actually completely gone.

Just as some women have hardly any pain in labour, and some have a great deal of agony, so there is a spectrum of physical symptoms around the menopause, from 'a rather slight physical experience' to quite a major one.

The physical sensations caused by the rebalancing of hormones at the menopause include hot flushes, night sweats, vaginal dryness, skin changes, loss of bone mass, and increased emotional vulnerability. If an initial read through this list makes you want to jump off the roof, keep calm, and consider the skill and strength you have already developed in your life; think about how you will use those resources to get the information and support you need to meet any such symptoms assertively. Let us look at them one by one.

Hot flushes and night sweats

These are the most frequently reported menopausal symptoms, known as 'hot flushes' in the daytime and 'night sweats' at night, but caused by the same 'vasomotor disturbance'. Generally, when our bodies overheat, our brain perceives this and sets into motion a mechanism which cools us down known as 'vasodilation', where the blood vessels near the surface of the skin dilate, and more blood flows through them, taking body heat with it to radiate out through the skin surface. The hot skin perspires and the perspiration evaporating on the skin has an added cooling effect.

For reasons not yet understood, during the climacteric communications between brain and skin can be disturbed, and the flushing and sweating reaction produced when the body isn't particularly hot. Hot flushes and/or night sweats are believed to be experienced by between 75 and 85 per cent of women at some time during their menopause. The frequency can vary from one a day or night to one an hour to several an hour. The flush itself can last between one and four minutes. It is believed that about 80 per cent of the women who experience hot flushes do so for two years or less, and the remaining 20 per cent have them for more than two years.

The 'flushing band' theory suggests that flushing occurs while a woman's oestrogen level is dropping through a middling 'band'. Above the upper limit and below the lower level of the 'band' there is no flushing. It is during the transitional time that the flushes happen.

Hazel said: 'I always felt conscious of my neck and throat being scarlet while I was flushing'; Moira said:

> I was acutely aware of having flushes in meetings at work. I felt as though I had a label hanging round my neck saying 'This women is going through the menopause'. It took all my determination to think 'it's a natural process I'm going through, there's nothing indecent about it, I just want to keep calm and carry on'.

How to cope

Develop a loose and many-layered style of clothing (it's particularly important to have open or loose necklines) so you can take layers on and off as you need to. When a flush comes on, breathe deeply and slowly into your abdomen to help yourself keep calm (see exercise 13, page 70). Some women carry an old-fashioned paper fan and use it to help cool off if a very hot flush comes over them. Others find it useful to buy a small desktop fan for the office.

If you are having hot sweats at night keep a couple of fresh towels and perhaps some cologne by the bed in case you need to rub yourself down during the night. If you are having hot flushes at night to the extent that you are regularly losing a lot of sleep, discuss it with your general practitioner.

Sheila Kitzinger, in *Woman's Experience of Sex*, records the moment where she moved into a more positive frame of mind about hot flushes:

> . . . a hot flush can look very attractive. I did not realize this until one day, as I had one, I went to a mirror and attempted to observe myself dispassionately. Though I felt odd, I liked the rosy glow. From that moment on I decided that hot flushes were life-enhancing.

She goes on to describe meeting the wave-like sensation of the flush with deep, slow breathing, and of enjoying a sense of 'going with' it rather than fighting it. It may be useful to use the image of 'breathing through' flushes as many of us 'breathed through' the contractions of our labours, and to have a vision of celebrating and feeling fully this womanly experience rather than fighting or denying it.

Vaginal dryness

As our oestrogen levels come down we may find that the walls of the vagina become thinner, drier, and less stretchy. This can make vaginal intercourse feel painful or tense. Sometimes we are more susceptible to infections of the urinary tract too and to stress incontinence (losing a little urine when we laugh, cough or exercise). These symptoms can be upsetting and threatening, but we can meet them and deal with them assertively and in our own time.

Difficulties with intercourse

Hesitancy and difficulty with intercourse can have multiple causes, some of them (perfectly legitimate) emotional ones to do with the relationship itself, which of course need addressing in their own right, but if you feel that physical vaginal dryness is a factor, there are steps you can take. Avoid irritating and drying soaps, bubble bath preparations or perfumed liquids in the bath water. Wear loosefitting clothes around the crotch, and cotton pants. Consider swapping your tights for stockings. Try using a vaginal lubricant (such as KY jelly or Senselle) when you make love. If this is not enough, oestrogen cream inserted into the vagina will thicken the vaginal walls and increase secretions (but see page 68). This has to be prescribed by your general practitioner. Once you feel relaxed and slippery again when you are making love, it seems that frequent lovemaking stimulates the vaginal walls and keeps them strong.

'Leaking'

If you are 'leaking' urine when coughing, laughing, or exercising, incorporate some pelvic floor exercises into your day. (In fact women should probably try to exercise their pelvic floor muscles daily throughout their lives.) The area we are discussing is the sling of muscles which lie in the area that would be covered by a sanitary towel, and you can feel two rings of muscle, one around your vagina and urethra, and one around your back passage. When you think about it, they are what is holding your insides in! If they have been doing this task for many decades, and perhaps had a few babies pushed out through them too, they deserve a bit of attention.

Imagine stopping the flow of urine, and holding in a bowel movement: this will cause you to squeeze your pelvic floor muscles. Relax them and they go back to normal again. Squeeze and release these muscles half-a-dozen times, several times a day. Tie the exercise to something you do frequently (using the phone, boiling a kettle) and you do many sets a day without it becoming a burden. Not only does this help to decrease incontinence (try coughing and jumping at the same time: if you don't leak, your pelvic floor is in good shape), it increases your sensual vaginal response because (a) your muscle tone is improved, and (b) you're more in touch with those muscles. If after doing these exercises regularly for a few weeks you are still frequently leaking, go and discuss it with your general practitioner.

Skin changes

See Chapter 5 for comments on changing skin and its care.

Bone changes

Bones in both men and women begin to decrease in density after the age of thirty, but after the menopause this process speeds up, because there is less of the oestrogen in our systems which helps us to retain calcium. The risk is that our bones become more porous and more brittle, and one in four elderly women develops osteoporosis which makes her bones extra vulnerable to fracture. As yet there is no way of predicting who are the 25 per cent of women who are at risk of osteoporosis, although it is a rare condition among black people and more common among Asian and white people. For information about hormone replacement therapy (HRT) see page 68.

The key ways we can help ourselves in this case are before the menopause: not to undereat or go on and off radical diets that might lesson our bone mass, and to keep up a sensible level of exercise, which improves bone density and mass. After the menopause it is useful to eat more calcium-rich foods (eggs, milk, cheese, yoghurt, fish, tofu, nuts, broccoli and kale).

Volatile emotions

So-called volatile emotions are unlikely to have a single, simple, hormonal cause. The responsibilities of a woman in her late forties and early fifties may be many and complex. They may include adolescent children, ageing parents, partner preoccupied with a peaking career, turning points and difficult choices in her own career. She also, as we have seen, has to make some sense of ageing in a youth-infatuated culture. If she has no children, she is faced with the final knowledge that she will never have them. If she is living without a partner, she has to try to evolve an interesting and fulfilling life in a couple-orientated culture.

With so many challenges in her life it seems unsurprising if she sometimes feels emotional. If that emotional disturbance is accentuated by fluctuating oestrogen levels, so much the tougher for her.

I would, however, like to make the point that many middle-aged men are also highly emotional – bad-tempered, unpredictable, demanding, and tense, but they tend to be excused this difficult package of behaviour as a result of pressures of work. It happens to them because of their daily foray into the industrial/professional jungle: they bravely go to provide their families, and our job is to soothe them – 'daddy's tired, daddy's worried, daddy's busy'. While one feels genuine sympathy and empathy for men in their middle years driven to emotional instability by pressure of work, we would have a different perspective (a) if men owned and took more responsibility for their emotions, and (b) if the work and multiple responsibilities in which women are engaged was acknowledged clearly.

If the emotional work of a busy life is made more difficult by fluctuating oestrogen levels it can feel dreadful. Moira said: 'I felt absolutely irrational. I was extremely worried about making decisions at work because I did not trust my own judgement at all. This went on for about eightcen months, then levelled out.'

Sheena said:

> I felt weepy. It reminded me of how easily fears would well up in my teenage years and in the early weeks of pregnancy. It annoys me that there is never anywhere to go in places of work to have a bloody cry. I can't be the only woman who

> would have found it useful just to be able to retreat for five minutes occasionally to have a bit of a cry and then pull myself together.

Hazel's life was crowded with sad events at the same time as her menopause, and the emotions all became woven together:

> Within eighteen months my husband died suddenly, my periods stopped, and my neighbour who was also my very good friend, also died. It was like two major griefs (the two deaths) and a minor one (the menopause). Life was just one long grieving process for a while.

Do not blame yourself for being emotional, but start to think what you want to do about it. You might want to address your emotions through counselling or therapy. You might want to find out if there is a 'menopause group' run by your local well woman centre (look them up in the phone book), or to have a chance to work out your feelings in a discussion or a therapy group with a more general brief.

It might be a good time to learn a new way of expressing yourself (see page 31) whether through 'creative' work, or movement, or some other new skill. As Christina says: 'It's the ability to go out and do new things on your own that is so strength-giving.' Kulsum (multicultural health consultant, forty) comments on the menopause:

> I have thought about the menopause – it's going to come. Then at least there's no pregnancy to worry about, I'll be a free spirit in that sense. It doesn't bother me – it's going to come so it might as well come. As far as my experience goes, many Asian women take the menopause very much in their stride, they don't see it as a crisis, they see it as part of life.

If you are in a part of your life where you feel so rotten you can hardly get up the high street on your own, let alone go and learn to sail a boat or hang glide, try to remember how many women have felt as you feel, and how they have come through that horrible transition period strengthened and moving into a new independence. Take it gradually, a step at a time, and seek support from friends, partners, therapists or groups, without embarrassment, if you need it.

Hormone replacement therapy

Feelings run high about this response to the menopause. Get as much information data and reaction as you can by reading and by networking through friends.

Hormone replacement therapy (HRT) describes the introduction of extra hormones into the bloodstream to replenish our waning oestrogen supply. This practice has been going on for nearly fifty years both here and in the United States. From the 1970s on oestrogen and progesterone together have been administered, since it was found that oestrogen alone carried an increased risk of cancer of the endometrium (lining of the womb).

HRT is given to three categories of women: those who want it and actively seek it; those who have severe menopause symptoms; and those who have early ovarian failure. It is not suitable for anyone with a history of high blood pressure, diabetes, migraine, epilepsy, nor for anyone who has had gallbladder disease, varicose veins, blood clotting or cancer anywhere in the body, or women who have a history of breast or uterine cancer in the family.

HRT can be given by means of oral tablets, vaginal creams, or small slow-release skin implants. The number of months or years it is used for is negotiated between the woman and her doctor. At the time of writing about 3 per cent of the menopausal population of the United Kingdom use HRT.

The benefits of using HRT are: an improvement in the specific menopausal symptoms and some protective effect in preserving bone mass and density; and sometimes an improvement in general frame of mind, similar to that seen in some women who 'feel wonderful' while they are pregnant. The qualms that women feel about HRT relate to anxiety that further side-effects may be shown to exist in future research, and also a distaste for interfering with a natural process.

Joan says: 'I think it's horrible mucking about with the natural process and I certainly don't intend to do anything of the sort.' But Hazel, although she generally avoids allopathic medicine, eats wholefood and runs what she calls with some humour a 'heavy brown household', says, 'I'm finding the lack of energy and muscle tone frustrating and annoying. I've had some good chats with my pleasant woman doctor and I'm now considering HRT.'

It seems important to weigh up the possible risks and benefits of HRT for you as an individual, and not to be swayed either into it by bland medical promises, or out of it by being made to feel not 'right-on'.

Exercise 10: Networking

Even if you are not menopausal yet, you can begin to acknowledge that it is an inevitable part of your cycle as a woman. Read about it, talk to other women about it. Deborah says:

> I knew nothing about the menopause all through school and college because I mixed only with young people. Now some of my colleagues are ladies in their forties and they naturally chat about these things. I find it really interesting – they are not morbid at all, they talk it over with a lot of humour, but I think the practical information and knowing what to expect will be really useful to me later on although it won't be for years and years yet.

If you are going through or have been through the menopause, don't be afraid to share your experiences with other women; networking is a way in which we can all give each other strength.

Exercise 11: The meaning

We all have to find the particular meaning of our own menopause. Using free drawing, writing, co-counselling, or discussion, or all of these things at different times, see if you can fathom out what the meaning of your menopause is to you, just as you will have worked to comprehend the meanings of your menarche, your fertility, labours, births, and other life passages before. It is a dignified respectable part of your life and does not need to be hidden.

Exercise 12: Laughter

Joy, active and elegant in her seventies, emphasizes the importance of keeping your sense of humour in good shape. Try and have a good laugh at least once a day! Read and share funny books and films, pin up cartoons that make you laugh, notice how making space for the light side of life, far from denying the serious currents, actually increases our understanding and ability to cope.

Exercise 13: Deep abdominal breathing

Sit comfortably either with your legs crossed or stretched comfortably out in front of you. Lift your spine, lengthen the back of your neck, lift the crown of your head. Release your shoulders, soften your face, let your eyes close.

Put one hand on your abdomen below your navel. Rest the other lightly on your knee.

Let your breathing settle into a steady rhythm. Breathe evenly and softly in through your nose and out through your mouth. Inhale and exhale at a steady rate.

When you have settled into a steady rhythm become aware of the hand on your stomach. As you breathe in, direct your breath down towards your hand. Feel your abdomen swell into your hand a little. As you exhale breathe all the way up from behind your hand. Feel your abdomen collapse back a little.

Breathing in, you fill up, and your abdomen swells into your hand. Exhaling, you empty, and your abdomen collapses back from your hand.

Carry on in your own rhythm, softly, steadily and evenly, breathing deep down into your hips. Do not gasp or blow, let the air *flow* in and out.

Notice how peaceful and calm you begin to feel.

After a few minutes (whenever it feels right to you) quietly take your hand away from your stomach and rest it on your knee. Let your breathing come back to an everyday level.

Become aware of your surroundings, and, when you feel like it, blink your eyes open. Don't rush, notice and enjoy the feeling of serenity this breathing brings before you move back into the activities of your day.

5

A Style of One's Own

'For me, a change of style means a change of intent, or a change in my inner self,' says Christine, 'but I often only notice in retrospect that a radical new haircut or wearing completely different clothes coincided with myself moving into a new phase. It's an unconscious thing.'

For some women, no longer being young and no longer being supposed to look like a pretty young woman is completely liberating.

'When I was younger I was conscious of being really ugly, not the "ideal" at all, but since I got past about my late thirties I just feel great, I accept my looks and I no longer have any wish to be "pretty" – I've just forgotten that whole issue,' says Maureen. She now wears

> bright colours, bright jewellery, loose shapes when I'm feeling bigger, tighter shapes when I'm feeling slimmer. I buy only things that I like (not things I think I ought to have), and things that don't make me look older. I feel a bit contradictory, in theory I don't particularly want to look other than my real age but in practice I'm pleased when people say 'you don't look your age', so I don't buy anything that would actually make me look older (sombre colours, staid styles) but I don't go looking for stuff to make me look *younger*. I do go for bright colours nowadays. I like to *flaunt* a bit.

Ann (thirty-eight, psychotherapist) also senses a change in her choices of colours. She says:

> I've moved from rather heathery tones towards bright ones. One of the things I'm enjoying at the moment is

> wearing black with brilliant colours – as I've come out more in myself I'm daring to wear more vibrant colours. I want a younger, more joyful image. I feel eager and ready for anything. It's quite a different kind of energy . . . I dress more sensually now than I did when I was younger.

This is echoed by a number of women – for example Joan (forty-two, senior lecturer in sociology):

> I am only just getting adjusted to the fact that I have a bosom! When I was eighteen I had short hair and was flat-chested. My mother and sister are both short in stature and have huge breasts, and I just couldn't bear the prospect of being like them. I remember them literally chasing me around the house with bras and sanitary towels that they wanted me to have, and I just wanted to deny the whole business. Later on I always wore high necklines and wanted to cover everything up. Now I really enjoy my female body shape and I don't try to hide it, and feel that showing my cleavage can be attractive without being a come-on. I don't go into 'younger' shops any more and I'm not trendy or fashionable, but I feel as though I know what suits me.

Perhaps it is their longer experience of life that is allowing these women to inhabit their bodies and their sexualities and therefore to enjoy their style more and choose clothes more confidently than they did in their teens and twenties.

Susan (fifty-four) feels that her mother constantly gives her accusing messages that she should 'dress her age'. She ignores them. However, in her fifties Susan has moved from a lifelong sense of 'looking wrong', and a feeling that even lovely clothes and textiles on hangers were given the kiss of death by coming near her, through a phase of making her own clothes and finding out what shapes and structures of clothes she really did like, to a very positive feeling about her own personal style.

I'm a varied person, so I wear varied clothes, but they must please me. If I feel fine, then I know other people will enjoy me. My clothes must be *really* comfortable and allow completely free movement. I'm interested in colour, and in texture. What I wear is direct, I'm not trying to project a particular colour or image. I used to be nervous about what people thought, but now I'm as adventurous as I want to be. I wear badges and brooches to make statements about issues I care about – peace badges, which have messages on, or an image that matters to me – creatures, birds, or natural scenes.

Kulsum (forty):

Muslim women's clothes are standard in shape so anyone can look good in them: the *khamis* and *shalwar* (tunic and trousers) or sari which has about 6½ yards of material in it, although you might wear different fabrics as you get older. I wouldn't wear a bright pink or a yellow any more.

One day when I was on a training course I thought I would have a bit of a change and wear a western skirt and blouse. For that day the women who were with me could not relate to me. I didn't mind, but I did notice; it wasn't a problem to me to change into western clothes, but it was a problem to my colleagues.

In my community, as you grow older you get more respect and more love, and people look to you for advice. I dress to reflect the wisdom that others expect me to have; although western colleagues say 'Do something about your hair, Kulsum, dye your hair', to us, these streaks of white hair are the badge of wisdom.

Hazel (remember her complaining: 'Who on earth wants to be able to wear *purple*?') describes her confusion:

I was a beatknik till I was forty, but it just didn't look right

> any more. Now I've softened my hairstyle, and because I've put on a stone in weight (which annoys me), I don't wear clinging clothes. I don't wear high heels because of liking to feel my whole foot on the floor. The style I have now – a bit ethnic-y – is just an interim. I'd like to be an old beatnik really – I have a *feel* of what I want, but I haven't made it happen yet.

Jane is also aware that she hasn't 'made it happen yet': 'Occasionally I wear things that look OK – I'm progressing at a slow pace towards that.' Jane is aware of using clothes to enhance her professional image and her confidence:

> When I'm working I always wear pearls, they're part of my signature. I've got both real and fake pearls. If I'm having a shaky day I wear the real ones! When I wear navy with pearls I look tremendously solid and knowledgeable. I was wearing a navy outfit and pearls in London the other day and at least twelve people asked me for directions!

She also derives confidence from the money value of clothes: 'I feel shaky at work in clothes that aren't expensive – expensive clothes make me feel better even if they actually look really horrible: and I always wear good shoes for work because I think people notice your shoes.'

Christina says frankly:

> I haven't found a style. I've changed, I'm still changing, but I'm not pleased. It must be great to think 'I feel good and I look good like this'. I look at people whose style I admire and wonder in amazement how on earth they manage it. On the other hand, I still like to be impulsive and make radical changes on a whim.

Hairdressers rank second only to medics as people who regularly disempower women from their assertive selves. In almost every effectiveness or assertiveness course I have run, many of them in a formal professional and not a personal context, at least one woman has dealings with hairdressers on her list of 'ten situations where I would like to be more assertive'. We're all familiar with simpering 'lovely' and leaving a heavy tip in the shop, and then going home to burst into tears!

As part of her 'younger, more joyful look' Ann says 'at last I've found a successful perm!' and certainly the chemistry of hair care and hair styling has been improved and refined in recent years. However, Jill's experience is more common: 'I go in wanting a really exciting style, and I see younger women walking out of the salon with terrific styles and I somehow get manoeuvred into something more moderate. I don't know if he's trying to tell me I'm too middle-aged for these haircuts or what.'

If you see a photograph somewhere of a style you want, cut it out and take it with you to the salon. You can discuss whether you can do that particular style with your particular hair, and also whether it will suit you or not. If you always come out of the hairdresser's cross and disappointed, ask around, keep trying until you find someone who does listen to what you say, and work out properly what you want. Remember to take into account how easy or complicated the style is going to be to look after. Joan says: 'My life changed after I met my new hairdresser! She just helped me see what I *could* do with my hair, and I don't dread going any more.'

You *are* an important enough person to get the haircut you want, practise your core phrases and assertiveness technique!

Skin care

Changing hormonal balances decrease the elasticity of our skin as we age, as does excessive exposure to sunshine.

In spite of the attempts of cosmetic companies to convince us otherwise, there appears to be very little we need to do to nourish our skins other than to moisturize regularly, and the cheapest most basic moisturizers seem to be equally effective as the expensive ones.

Almost all the women interviewed expressed a preference either on ethical or religious grounds (or both) for products not tested on animals and not containing whale products; many major manufacturers have found the force of public opinion has persuaded them to follow the example of Body Shop, Beauty Without Cruelty, and others, and make products which fulfil these conditions.

Many women had made a conscious decision not to wear makeup because: 'I no longer want to appear to be anything other than I am'. But, equally, many women enjoy using makeup and one even sees it as a source of energy: 'When I use makeup, I don't think of it as beautifying or hiding – I think: I'm going out to face the world and this is my warpaint.'

Skin has its own poetry – it is the boundary or barrier between ourselves and the outside world, and it is one of our primary ways of experiencing the world outside ourselves. Soreness, sensitivity, and rashes, as well as their 'objective' causes, may have something to say about pain and difficulty in understanding our boundaries or managing the interface between inside-yourself and outside-yourself.

The following are some exercises to help you find your own personal style in clothes, hair and general image.

Exercise 14: Favourite clothes

If you want to share this exercise with a friend, have five minutes each to talk about your favourite item of clothing (shoes, hats and jewellery can also be included in this category). Describe it and say what it means to you and what it says about you. It might be a new and glamorous piece of clothing, or something old that has been with you through all sorts of things. Choose whatever comes spontaneously into your mind as your favourite item. If you currently don't have anything you like, choose something you have owned in the past which you particularly loved, or something you would like to have now but don't.

If you are working on this on your own, write or draw (or both) a description of clothes you love or have loved. Make notes on why you loved them.

This simple exercise reveals a lot about the conscious and unconscious structures surrounding clothes and presentation for us.

Exercise 15: Colours

As in exercise 14, do this either with a friend or if on your own make notes, and sketches or patterns too if you want.

The range of colours in which you dress is highly expressive. What kind of colours do you tend to wear? Why? What do they say about you? Is it a different spectrum from colours you have worn in other parts of your life? How do you feel about this? How does it feel to imagine yourself in quite different colours? Are there any changes you want to make about the kind of colours you choose?

Give yourself some time to reflect, talk and write about the colours you use.

Exercise 16: Making your own . . .

If you have a lifelong skill in dressmaking you will be aware of the financial savings possible, and the opportunity to have your own original clothes. If you have felt defeated by paper patterns you might at some point consider making your own patterns with newspaper or tissue from any clothes of a simple shape you particularly like, so that you can make copies of a favourite shape in other fabrics, or buying in your own size and in the most basic form possible, the patterns for, say, a full-flared skirt, loose trousers, a simple square jacket, and a simple 'top'. Then if you come across any particularly lovely fabric you can, when you feel like it, make a garment out of it. I am not in a sewing phase at the moment – for me it's a skill that comes and goes – but I enjoy the style and impact of a colleague who buys entirely intuitively, remnants from Liberty's, Habitat curtain fabrics, and other stores, and having designed a few basic garments that suit her shape, has a dazzling and enviable wardrobe at half the price of items available at chain stores and free of their narrow range of styles.

Pattern cutting courses at adult education night school will give you the basic skill at cutting the shape of garments you want, if you can't find anything that suits you in the commercial pattern range; and even if formal dressmaking is not your thing at all, we can all bear in mind that we may at times find more freedom and fun in making our own clothes.

Exercise 17: De-stressing clothes size

Consider these points:

1. The current sizing system in shops is both recent and fairly arbitrary, and over half the women in the United Kingdom are over size 16, although you wouldn't think so to look at the stock in many shops.
2. The general availability of antibiotics is responsible for the current svelte ideal figure. We can only afford to be so light now that we don't need a spare stone or so of weight to fight any infection we develop. Paul Poiret the great French designer of the 1920s described his ideal models as six feet tall and eleven stone in weight and he was the designer who, almost single-handedly, got women out of corsets, so he was not thinking of eleven corsetted stone. The current ideal would be almost six foot tall but barely eight stone.

Until after the Second World War when standardized sizes and mass production became general, garments for bourgeois and aristocratic women were made in separate and individually fitted sections: skirt, bodice, and sleeves, all adjusted to each woman. Women are no more a standard size now than they were then, but any of us not the same shape as shop clothes often feel deeply humiliated, not to mention frustrated that we can never buy anything that fits all over.

Furthermore, many of us develop a mystical attachment to the number of the size on the label. We will suffer tight waistbands and straining buttonholes in order to know that we are wearing a 16 rather than an 18 or a 10 rather than a 12. If the size labels in your clothes oppress you, cut them out of the clothes and then throw them away and forget about them. A woman at ease with her body and able to breathe and move comfortably and fluently in her clothes will always look lovely, whatever her hip measurement is.

6
Facing Up To Death

The death rate in any country, however affluent, remains 100 per cent. Our western materialist culture is very uncomfortable about this. With ever-falling infant mortality and, generally, increasing capacity for fighting disease, many grown-up people have never seen a dead body, never had a death among their family and friends, never learned anything at all about bereavement, loss, and mourning, or, faced with the death of someone close, thought about getting in touch with their own death.

It is hard for us to evolve a philosophy to cope with the end of our lives, when we have grown up in a context in which our chief value would seem to be our individuality and our uniqueness. The thought of that individuality coming to a full stop can be terrifying.

This is not the case in the same way for members of the community who have a faith or a religion which integrates death with life and does not hide it.

Kulsum:

> I think religion makes a great impact, you are always aware that there is this thing death, and you must think of it because it can come any time. We prepare our children, it is a matter of fact, and when there is a death in the family our children go through that upset too, and they see the body. I have seen death become a terror in the West, where children are protected from it when they are younger, and then they cannot cope when they are older. . . . I believe that life is like getting on a train, but that the destination is somewhere else: so death to me is a very acceptable part of life.

We might come to many different kinds of resolutions and insights about the ending of our lives, but certainly becoming familiar with the truth that our lives will end, and with the feelings that arise in us about that, are part of the task of life. They come more readily to our minds once we move into the phase which we know is the second, and final, half of our lives.

Some women have experienced the deaths of parents or grandparents in such a frightening way when they themselves were very young that they faced a terror about which they were unable to communicate, and where, unlike Kulsum's family and community, there was no philosophy available to begin to make sense of the experience.

Such a frightening contact with death in the family, without appropriate support and opportunities to talk, ask questions, and be comforted, can lead the child to feel that his/her own hold on life is very tenuous.

After her grandfather died when she was in her early teens, Christina said:

> I used to lie awake at night afraid to go to sleep, because I was afraid that if I did I would stop breathing. His death coincided with my move to senior school. I had failed to get into grammar school and so I was already fairly anxious. My anxiety reached such a point that I also used to find it difficult to breathe in school assembly, and thought I was about to die there. My daughter (age five) talks a *lot* about dying and I encourage her to when she wants to. I hope it will de-terrorize it for her. Myself I've always been very frightened of physical danger since those days – you could say I was 'scared of living and frightened of dying' – but the sailing course I did this year was a breakthrough where I finally went and did something very physical, fairly risky, and survived.

For Joan the sudden death of her father at the age of forty

when she was in her early teens had a long-lasting effect on her opinion about her own ability to survive.

> I watched my father drive along the road and turn in through the drive to our house, but instead of straightening the car up, he just continued to drive in a circle until the car ended up in the ditch. We ran out to see him slumped over the wheel and a neighbour very tactlessly and brutally told me he was obviously already dead. He had had a heart attack.
>
> I behaved like a heroine in a schoolgirl novel – I was the strong one who looked after my mother and everyone assumed I had got over my feelings about his death and that the pain had been brief for me, but I had not really got over it at all. After my father died I used to feel I was dying while I was falling asleep. My grief didn't finally hit me with full force until I left home and went to university.
>
> When I was pregnant with my first child in my early thirties, a routine check showed I had a cystolic heart murmur. This increased my fear of dying at forty of a heart condition like my father's (my grandfather had also died at forty of a heart attack). Part of me became convinced that I too would die at forty.
>
> My biggest fear was what would happen to my children: it wasn't the end of my own life that frightened me so much as what would happen to those left behind.
>
> The one person I have not shared this with is my general practitioner. I did not ask whether the murmur was still there during my second pregnancy and I avoid having my heart checked, although I do watch both diet and exercise and I am hyper-aware of any pains or odd sensations in my chest.
>
> On my fortieth birthday I had a big party and then went to France on holiday. Since I did not drop dead at the party, which I half expected to do, I have become less and less preoccupied with death and feel I may survive for a long time.

One clear message for all of us is to remember that children who appear to have 'got over' a death among friends or family may in fact be holding an awful lot of feelings in. Another is to acknowledge that our own childhood experiences of death may be influencing the way we attempt to handle the subject of death now, and to have a good look at them (with proper support and counselling if we feel we need it) if we suspect they may need our attention.

Hazel's attitude to death has developed to a deep understanding and knowledge through her varied experiences:

> I was a nurse for twenty years and so I encountered death continually, and my attitude changed profoundly over those years. When I think of myself as a twenty-year-old student nurse laying out my first person who died, I'm amazed really, I was almost callous, very detached, it was just a task I had to do. I'm so grateful for nursing training and experience as a nurse though, I think it's the most powerful training anyone could possibly have, and you really get close to the powerful things in life. It made death part of my life. I had to think about it and come to terms with it.
>
> I was with my husband when he died. It was the most amazing experience. I was so glad I was there. The loneliness in which some people die shocks me: I wanted to be there, to say goodbye. You wouldn't not say goodbye when they went on any other journey would you?

Hazel experienced the death of her husband and that of her best friend, as well as her own menopause, all in the same year, when she herself was in her late forties. She has spent a lot of time grieving and studying death and grief. She has a lot of books on the subject. She does not belong to a church although she says she would like to, but cannot find a form of organized religion that suits her. However, she does not believe 'that death is death and that's the end. I feel it's part of the round of nature and part of the round of nature that *I'm* part of. I have strong but not clearly defined feelings about reincarnation which I have a sense probably happens.'

Hazel's sense of a kind of organic reintegration (as being part of the 'round of nature') links in with Susan's understanding:

> I have two distinct ways of thinking about death. One way is that it's part of the cyclic process of nature. Nature (in air, water, food, and so forth) is moving into and out of my body all through my life, and so dying is part of the materials I have borrowed from the universe going back into use by my fellows or by animals or plants, or being reintegrated into the planet in some way. That feels fine. That aspect of dying feels very like living. . . . Another aspect is one I have heard, and felt in myself, in people talking either about deaths or dead parts of their lives: a bleak howling loneliness, an anti-existence. I live alongside this aspect and accept it – there are traces of it in all sorts of bits of life, as when something is horribly wasted.

Both Jane and Ann have been in touch with the 'bleak howling loneliness' without having a feeling of healing and reintegration, and for both of them it was connected with the months immediately after childbirth. Ann says:

> In the first year of my first child's life, from the moment he was born, I had to recognize that with life came death. I had never considered mortality before, my inner process had been a denial of death. I had bad apocalyptic holocaust-type dreams. I got hysterical every time I saw a car accident. All this caused a depression that I couldn't shift and I couldn't ignore. Death as an archetype had suddenly arrived. I was learning a lesson but I was learning it too fast. I'm standing back now, considering it all more slowly.

Death terrified Jane:

> . . . it pops out like something nasty out of the woodwork, especially since I've become a parent: seeing that life has a beginning made it clear to me that it also had an end. I've read Elisabeth Kubler Ross, but it doesn't help, nothing helps, I can't get to grips with the fact that I will one day cease to be. It makes me feel guilty about the time I waste and the time I wish away, every moment ought to be precious. . . . I am drawn closer to a religion or a belief in God which I was very dismissive about. I made a sort of deal with God that if my second child (born when I was thirty-six) was OK, God could 'have' me – she was, and I feel I sort of owe Him one.

Even with a sense of possible reintegration, or reincarnation, or movement into another sphere, the ending of this life can seem extremely sad; if the time following death seems to you to be a howling void, it can feel like a catastrophe. Facing the end, trying to become familiar with the ending, is a project long undertaken by philosophers and creative artists. Looking for inspiration among their work is a personal and individual business, but generally it is useful not to shy away from images of, explorations of, accounts of death and dying, and, if it's your cup of tea, of transcendence too.

At the time of writing several major air disasters, the King's Cross fire, the Clapham train crash, the San Francisco earthquake, all conspire to remind us that we live in soft, fragile, breakable bodies, of blood, muscle, bone, sinew, marrow. We all share a vulnerable, tenuous presence here, and any death shows us our own, any death could have been ours.

John Donne is a seventeenth-century poet who speaks to us clearly today, his passionate sexuality running alongside his preoccupation with comprehending death in a strangely modern way.

> No man is an island, entire of himself; every man is a piece of the Continent, a part of the main; if a clod be washed away by the sea, Europe is the less, as well as if a promontory were. . . ; any man's death diminishes me, because I am involved in Mankind. . . . And therefore never send to know for whom the bell tolls; It tolls for thee. (*Meditation* XVII)

Robert North's choreography of 'Death and the Maiden' for the repertoire of London Contemporary Dance Theatre came out of his own reflections about death, as he explained on *Dancemakers* (BBC, 1985). Dancers obviously have a particularly vibrant relationship with their own bodies, and are particularly moved by contemplating the loss of those bodies. North described his own feeling that we should have our own deaths in mind and as much as possible have it by our side like a brother/sister or a *doppelgänger*, making friends with it as best as we can. His ballet shows death in many aspects – as a shocking event, a sudden event, a process causing physical pain, a process giving release, relief and love.

Glimpses into a transcendent vision for anyone who senses it as a possibility are there in thousands of places:

> The self cannot be pierced by weapons or burned by fire; water cannot wet it, nor can the wind dry it. . . . It is everlasting and infinite, standing on the motionless foundations of eternity. The self is unmanifested, beyond all thought, beyond all change. Knowing this, you should not grieve. O mighty Arjuna, even if you believe the self to be subject to birth and death, you should not grieve. Death is inevitable for the living; birth is inevitable for the dead. Since these are unavoidable you should not sorrow. (*Bhagavadgita*, 2, 23–27)

Faure's *Requiem* and Mozart's *Requiem Mass* are among the musical responses to death which while they hold the sadness of death also soar with 'the hope of the life to come'.

Anyone, who like Hazel, has to say a difficult goodbye, may want to share a poem from the first century BC. Catullus had made a long journey to his brother's grave:

> Through many people, over many seas I come,
> my brother, to your piteous grave.

Catullus felt that his living brother had been torn away from him by cruel fate. All that is left is to bring the ritual death offerings.

> Take these gifts, brought as our fathers' bade
> Sorrows' tribute to your grave,
> Take my flood of brother's tears,
> and for eternity, brother, hail and farewell.

These fragments of my own 'death anthology' will not, of course, be to everybody's taste or be coherent with everybody's philosophy. They are simply there to suggest the broad spectrum of sources for help and illumination one may find by allowing the subjects around death through one's habitual filter or censoring defence mechanism, when in contact with music, poetry, the visual, tactile, and movement arts such as mime and ballet.

Exercise 18: Making friends with your death

Using individual work (free drawing, writing, etc.), and pair work (co-counselling, discussion) take Robert North's idea of 'making friends with your own death', and having it walk alongside you, like a familiar or a *doppelgänger*, rather than a terrifying monster you rarely look in the face. Think (talk, write, draw) about what it means to you to have the kind of daily awareness Kulsum talks about ('death is always in our minds because it can come any time') without the accompanying feelings being morbid or panicky.

If getting in touch with an awareness of death begins to overwhelm you or fill you with horror, spend some time with some of the beautiful creative and philosophical work that has been done around death. Seek the help of a trusted friend, or if none is available, call the Samaritans, whose local number is in the phone book (their aim in providing a twenty-four-hour 365-day cover is precisely that no-one should have to face a sense of hopelessness entirely alone). There is of course a sense in which we all have to face death alone, but it is a great point for sharing that since we all have to die, we all have to work out some kind of comprehension and acceptance, and in that common ground, we can all try to give each other support.

Exercise 19: Partings and separations: a good-enough goodbye

The goodbye we say to another person who is dying, and the goodbye that they say to us, is important. We would like it to be perfect and complete, but of course it often isn't.

With parents, partners, friends, there may be 'unfinished business', repressed emotional matters, unspoken angers, questions unasked and unanswered. Perhaps the more intense the relationship the more unworked-out material there may be. In this I suppose there is a clear sense that death is like life – messy, ambiguous, complex.

It *is* sometimes a time where some people feel able to say things clearly to one another and *make* clear their love for one another, but it may not necessarily be like that. If you are spending time with someone who is dying, all you can do is be as real as you can, listen well, share, and say anything loving or affirmed that you can.

If the person is dying over a period of time you may well feel that the person that was them left some time before their physical body finally dies. You may need to take your leave twice in that situation, once, as it were, when the person is gone and again when their body does not work any longer. It is hard to do.

If the person dies suddenly you may be left with having said a horrible goodbye because it was not clear that it was goodbye. One woman reports in Kitzinger's *Woman's Experience of Sex*: as her teenage son left the house she yelled after him 'And for goodness sake, wash your hands!' He was killed later that day in a car crash, so those were her last words to him. Fate seems very cruel when one parts with a careless snarl or argument, then loses the person forever. The only recourse is to try to see the story and flavour of the relationship as a whole, and although being sorry about unpleasant parting words, to know the warp and weft of years of involvement add up to far more than that.

We can think over, with support if necessary, our ability to say 'goodbye', make an ending and part. I have a lot of work to do here, finding any goodbye which implies more than a few hours' separation almost unbearable. At the moment, two elements are helpful to me – one is an evasive move, where I always arrange to leave before the other person realizes the separation is going to take place – my patterns are full of leaving places and people prematurely – but this is hardly a constructive approach; the other is a growing sense that where your life has overlapped with someone else's you are never completely lost to each other – having absorbed something of each other's presence and ideas, you are never wholly separated. However, this may seem to be a facile rationalization – if so, discard it, but look for your own form and construction on how to accept separations and goodbyes, most of all the difficult goodbye of death. We can rarely expect to be able to say a completely reconciled goodbye – but sometimes may be able to try to say a good-enough goodbye.

Exercise 20: Anthology

The word 'anthology' comes from two Greek words: 'anthae' (flowers) and 'logoi' (words). So an anthology is the flowers of words that we may choose from the morass of words (or images or whatever) that we experience every day. Given the presence of flowers in most of our rituals surrounding death, an 'anthology' of creative responses to death seems very appropriate. Allow yourself to notice, respond to, and collect anything in any medium on the subject of death that you find positive, thought-provoking, moving, or helpful in any way.

7
Age and Rage

We have spent much of our time considering ageing so far in terms of emphasizing the positive, and, where we found unavoidable negatives, finding positive ways of responding to them. Nevertheless, we must make some time to be unequivocally negative, angry, raging, incensed, and furious. We must have some chances to stop behaving ourselves and let rip. When you get sick of trying to flow with the universe in a generous, positive way, use this chapter to let your shadow side out for a while to stamp, scream, and bare its teeth.

Women described rage or incipient rage about various issues.

Jane says her work as a management consultant often leaves her as one, or one of a couple of young lively women in a large group of older men:

> I meet a lot of men in my work and I'm always the belle of the ball, so there's a built in system of 'strokes' for me. I realize that someday soon I'll fancy someone younger and they'll go off with someone younger and prettier than me who does the work better than I do. I have an awareness that this will happen, but I don't have a plan. I just know it's going to be a hell of a jolt when it happens.

The communal changing rooms of high street clothes shops give Charlotte ample cause for rage:

> Somehow when I am struggling to force my vibrating jellylike flesh into some garment, I am surrounded by sylph-like teenagers in glamorous underwear (mine is always grey and overstretched) who are sliding effortlessly into lovely skirts or trousers. I feel so angry that I'm not like

> them just because I've had children, just because I'm twenty years older, just because I haven't got the time to look after my body and my looks any more. In fact I don't remember ever looking like them even when I *was* their age. It's so unfair that some people just get a lovely body handed to them. I could scream. I often give up the attempt to buy clothes at that point anyway and go home miserable, and as likely as not stuff myself with cake and feel even worse.

Melanie speaks of two flashes of anger – one is about shortage of time for achieving what she wants to, and the other is a feeling that her body is beginning to disintegrate before she has time fully to inhabit it. It's a sense of having got to know herself and her own needs more clearly in her forties, but the time to act on her insights is now terribly short.

> I feel a stab of jealousy seeing children and children's friends blithely going off on long courses of training, even taking a year off, and knowing they have plenty of time. My teenage children laugh if I ask them what they will be doing next month – it seems such a long way ahead to them that they can't imagine why you might even *want* to plan that far ahead, let alone have any idea where you're going to be and what you're going to be doing. The months flick past as far as I'm concerned like express trains. I'm almost beginning to feel like that about the *years*.
>
> I'm also bitter that having only just, through the women's movements and women's groups, begun to accept my body, it seems to be beginning to fall apart. I'm bitter about all the lost years where, although young and healthy, I didn't enjoy my body at all, and now I've come to like it, it almost seems too late, I've got to accept that it's ageing.

The deteriorating illnesses which may come in old age were most people's worst fear about age – worse in some ways than terror of death. (Compare the war artist Linda Kitson's observation of soldiers in the Falklands: '. . . the ultimate fear which I noticed for most men was the fear of being maimed forever. They really were more scared by the thought of a major physical setback for life than of dying.') It is an irony of modern medicine, that, preserved from the catastrophic diseases which killed our grandmother's and great grandmother's generations, we may face a process of slow disintegration from which we recoil. Although we probably all agree with Joan that 'my own will is a factor in not deteriorating', and that activity, involvement, courage and intellectual toughness may all contribute, society as a whole with an ageing population, and we ourselves as individuals, may have to face the dilemmas posed by the wasting diseases that are possible in old age.

Catherine described her anger about the 'wrong' people dying as one of the vivid experiences of her late fifties. She found particularly that the death of her husband who was a kind, clever, and intuitive man, left her enraged at the continuing life of people whom she regarded as irresponsible timewasters who did not deserve any more time. She described many sleepless anguished nights battling with the unfairness of it all. Acceptance came slowly and only provisionally: 'I still think he was worth ten of most of the individuals around me, and I cannot comprehend why he had to die while they are still living,' she says, 'but it is not like a knife in the side all the time any more.' I would like to mention that although Catherine's words are bitter, the aura around her as a person is peaceful and gentle.

Susan feels angry that she is often forced to be 'mature' because of the irresponsibility of younger people – that is, she resents the business of being in the place where the buck stops in terms of domestic matters, organization, bill-paying, catering and laundry. Although she tries not to let the younger people in her household lean on her in this way, it is often a battle. Her remedy is 'to find time to be really silly when I can, to get away from the relentless pressure to do the Right Thing'.

Rage is a hard emotion to own and express. Instead of loud energy-giving *out*-rage we often have *in*-rage which can be inwardly destructive: its energy blowing up inside ourselves rather than in the world outside. Outwardly expressed out-rage is often mocked as overreaction and hysteria. However, at its best anger is a source of enlightenment and energy which tells us there is something wrong in our lives, that we need to work out what it is, and produces the initial burst of energy needed to do something about it.

If you want to get in touch with a jet of powerful rage, read Mary Daly's book *Gyn/Ecology* – much of the abuse of women it describes is so appalling that it is hard to read, but it certainly connects one with a strong clear passion of righteous out-rage about the way women are treated in many different cultures. It clears away completely the sense that any women's movement anywhere may have been overreacting to circumstances. Rage suppressed, rage combined with helplessness, makes for depression; but we can work on using our fury at the gross abuses described by Mary Daly to see the need for changes in our lives, our microcosms, our families, our inner image of ourselves, now, and to have the energy and inner power to carry them out.

Exercise 21: 'What would happen if I got angry. . . ?'

Because it's not 'nice' to be angry, as children told not to be we may have developed frightening fantasies of what would happen if we did become angry. We may have carried these fantasies forward in some form or another into our adulthood. Maybe you can begin to unhook yourself from these fantasies by finding out what they are and observing and reflecting on them. If you are working with a friend, sit comfortably opposite one another and have five minutes to take turns to say sentences beginning:

'If I got angry. . . .'

Take your time, have as long gaps between goes as you need to. Say what you hear coming into your head from your instinctive, child, or dream level, and try not to let your intellect censor it (for example with 'that's silly', 'she'll think I'm silly', or 'that's ridiculous').

If you are working alone use free writing and drawing to make sentences and pictures about what 'would happen' if you got angry.

In pairs, or on your own, when you have got in touch with what your images and fantasies are, take some time to think about them, and see what they have to say to you.

If I got angry the house would blow up.
If I got angry my mother would shrivel up and die like the Witch at the end of *The Wizard of Oz*.
If I got angry my husband would leave me.
If I got angry I would get hotter and hotter and hotter until my skin started to blister and come off in shreds.
If I got angry I would start to shout and I would never, ever be able to stop.
If I got angry I would be incapable of doing my job.
If I got angry nobody would like me.
If I got angry I would then get very sad.
If I got angry a crack would open in the earth with fire inside and I might fall in.

Would anger make you unlovable? *Would* it have a magic evil power that would destroy people or things around you? Consider what must have been happening to your child-self to give you the impression that this is the way the world works. If you have been blackmailed or misled in this way, consider how you feel about it now. Share your thoughts with your partner or make drawings or write about how you feel.

If this exercise leaves you badly rattled or un-centred, as I have said repeatedly throughout the book, bear in mind that you may want some support, either informally by confiding in or sharing with a friend, or in a more structured way with counselling or therapy. If you feel upset and miserable and are alone and unable to get in touch with a friend, put some peaceful music on and do the deep relaxation exercise (page 55) or turn to the end of the book and read through the 'Meditation on the Great Peace' (page 105).

Return to your thoughts about 'If I got angry . . .' in the days and weeks to come, when you feel ready to.

Exercise 22: Assertive anger

Once we are a little more free of the fear that expressing anger will provoke some sort of global cataclysm, we can begin to find assertive ways of expressing our anger. Sometimes it is anger with other people, sometimes it is anger with institutions or society as a whole. Sometimes it is anger with ourselves.

The basis of assertiveness is to form a strong central self-image and self-respect, and to be able to act some of the time at least in a way that is strong and effective without being either aggressive, sarcastic, or in a passive state.

To turn our anger into a positive force for shaping our lives we can use assertiveness principles. First: by the use of a 'core phrase': that is by making a clear statement that expresses what we want to say without equivocation or apology. It could be:

1. 'I am very angry that you are treating me in this way';
   or,
2. 'I am very angry that images of women are exploited in the tabloid press';
   or,
3. 'I am angry with myself for never managing to sign on for the exercise class I am always talking about.'

It may be a sentence that we intend at some point actually to say to someone, or one that we need to form clearly in order to have a name for what we feel.

It is also quite possible that one's sentence would be something like: 'I feel angry and at the moment I am not clear why. The reason for this is not that I am stupid. It is that both society and individuals are complex and I am not yet sure where my anger comes from.'

(A liberating act for many women is to form the habit of thinking that if you feel something it is because something is *making* you feel that way and not because you are hypersensitive.)

Telling someone assertively that you are angry will not cause them to blow up or drop dead. It may well open up a discussion about how to improve the situation (for a description of how to avoid getting 'hooked' into irrelevant arguments at this point, see Anne Dickson's book *A Woman in Your Own Right*). Try something like: 'I'd like us to work out together how we might be able to change things.'

If you are angry with society as a whole as in example 2 above, you need to own and respect your anger and then decide what you want to do about it. It is unlikely that you can change the structures in society that lead to that kind of abuse in one fell swoop, but you can exert your own influence in your own sphere, and this should not be underestimated. The rippling outward circles of how one person behaves with another and how this affects how they behave with the next person with whom *they* interact, is the warp and weft of how things happen in the world.

The way I speak, relate to people, dress, the jokes I will and won't laugh at, the language I use, can all have some effect on the way the people around me perceive women, and also how they perceive the (ab)use of women in the media.

If some of your anger is social, think about how you can be effective in shifting attitudes around you, as well as clearly owning your righteous anger. As you gain in confidence and self-esteem you will find that you are more able to express anger in debate, social situations, and the workplace, without being the victim of ridicule and contempt. It is exciting to feel your anger turn into power and influence instead of something which hurts you inside and only seems to draw fire onto you on the outside. Enjoy the new sense of strength that comes from believing in your own judgement and intelligence, and speaking out your anger in a forthright way.

Look now at example 3. An assertive extension of that core phrase might be:

> Until now it has not been a high enough priority for me to make exercise part of my life. I have been surviving and coordinating things in the best way for me up until now and there has not been space. This is the time I want to decide to make space and let some other things and people come lower on the list or priorities.

The point I am trying to make is to own the anger or frustration you feel about your behaviour, but to avoid the trap of turning it into a generalized criticism of yourself and general self-flagellation session ('I'm always hopeless about this kind of thing'), and to affirm some positive intention and action.

Use this exercise to elucidate any angers you feel at the moment, not just those that are obviously about ageing. They will be linked with your feelings about ageing in some way if you are finding out about them in this context, and you can track them back to the subject of ageing as and when you want to. This is often true of exploratory exercises. One seems to be going off at a tangent, but follow any genuine feelings that arise, because they will have (sometimes quite unexpected) connections with the theme you began with which will emerge eventually.

Exercise 23: Dancing your shadow

It is possible to conceive of the human personality as an inclusive whole which has a dark side as well as a light one.

Both Jungian psychology and the Oriental philosophy of

the Tao acknowledge a shadow side in everyone, a side that balances compassion, gentleness, and peace with violence, greed and the negative emotions. As carers, nurturers, and supporters, our shadow side can become very submerged. It is interesting to be more in touch with the dark side which will certainly come through from time to time in any creative activities with which you are involved, such as dancing, painting, writing.

In the mid-1970s the punk style gave a spectacle (or so I thought) of young people walking around dressed up in their shadow archetype – and some of the other styles like the 'Gothic' look, or the much more violent skinhead image display aspects of the same thing.

Meeting and knowing our own shadows does not imply a descent into violence or anarchy but a fuller acceptance of the whole spectrum of ourselves.

8
Strategies for the Second Half

This final chapter seeks to give a framework in which you can work out your own strategy for your second half, after the explorations and investigations of previous chapters. Such a strategy will be flexible and renewable, of course, and will have a different feel about it from individual to individual, according to family circumstances, health, resources, time, career, and so on and so forth. One will want to change one's mind from time to time in some areas and update in others. As we said in the first chapter, planning for the experience of ageing is hardly the sole and central desired occupation of our lives from thirty onwards – but ignoring or denying the physical, mental, and spiritual challenges of ageing may leave us ill-equipped to do with our lives the things we really do want to do.

Both Kulsum and Hazel emphasize the importance of thinking positively, both for social and philosophical reasons. Kulsum says:

> I just won't feel negative about it. In my community it is not likely I will be marginalized. When my childen were defenceless I looked after them and when I am old they will look after me. . . . The best thing to do with ageing is to take it as it comes. If you feel you're slowing down and can't do one kind of thing, find something else you *can* do. Meet and talk to other women, share how you feel. It's life, it's nature, accept it – we may as well grow old with dignity accepting the whole thing.

Hazel's comment is:

> I feel we must be positive about ageing, we're bloody lucky to be alive. We shouldn't whinge because life is such a gift. I'm in a very privileged middle-class situation to have time to be reflecting on how ageing feels.
>
> After being sterilized I was in a hospital bed opposite two women who were absolutely high being in hospital having hysterectomies, because this was the first time they had got away from the demands of their families for about twenty years! It was a real holiday for them! It's things like that that make me realize how lucky I am, how little cause I've got to complain.

I see positive thinking as an obviously useful skill to practise, and take both Kulsum's advice to concentrate on what you *can* do, not what you *can't* do, and Hazel's point about appreciating whatever easy passages there have been in your life and celebrating the unique chance to be here, now.

Joan noticed how at least one really significant positive project has come up each decade for her:

> I went to university when I was twenty, had my first child at thirty and will publish my first book in my early forties. Perhaps I should aim finally to finish my PhD when I'm fifty and maybe I'll write a novel when I'm sixty! Seriously though, I think if you set yourself a really positive project every five or ten years, if you're in the kind of work or the kind of lifestyle that will allow you to do so, it helps mark the time out and prevent you from feeling that it's sliding by you in a way that you can't control. It gives you a growing confidence in yourself as a person who sets herself targets and achieves them, and the targets themselves could be in a variety of areas, not just based on work.

Catherine (seventy) undertook a new career while living in the United States because of her husband's job:

> I qualified as a real estate broker at the age of fifty-seven. It was a real achievement to me – it put me in touch with a totally different world becoming a businesswoman. I was amazed to find that not only could I do it, I was very good.

Catherine also sees an ability to follow up new opportunities and interests as very important to her own good experience of moving through new ages, and cites a friend who: 'is getting an Open University degree soon, and she's late into her eighties, she's full of interest and enquiry still'.

When asked what insights she would pass onto other women from her experience of ageing Catherine says: 'I'm not one to give advice because people's lives are so individual. However, the best thing is to keep your mind busy. Also, express yourself from time to time. Be a bit impulsive if you feel like it!'

Christina's vision from close to the midpoint of life is:

> I see life as a journey, and that in every age there's something in it for you to enjoy. It's all mysterious, but we have to try to understand it. As a woman anyway you are constantly adapting to what's happening in your family. You learn to cope with a complete upheaval of focus quite regularly and I think that must be a good tool for learning to deal with the changes coming through age. I think it teaches you that you need something outside your family to sustain you through the changes. I sometimes feel that as you move on you just get the necessary inner strength. It comes.

Exercise 24: Forming a strategy

We could set out our strategy for the second half thus:

Making a personal, considered relation with our ageing process:

- affirming our experience and achievements
- making a commitment to an 'extracurricular' activity

- making a commitment to finding out about health
- making a commitment to knowing and loving our bodies
- making a commitment to our right to express ourselves
- making a commitment to familiarizing ourselves with our own death
- moving away from ageism – seeing older people in our circle as people in their own right
- with an increasing ageing population, understanding as a society the general need for work on positive ageing.

Using co-counselling, discussion, or notes and drawing, take each of those themes in turn and consider where you stand on it now, and how you would like to develop in this area.

I began writing this book feeling anxious, upset and angry about my own ageing. I felt fearful of the loss of power in society that I anticipated upon the loss of youthful looks and aura. I could not envision a way to age which was not either a completely passive capitulation (what our mothers' generation used to call 'letting yourself go') or a frantic investment of time, energy, and money in fending off the ageing process with denial and panic.

The contact with so many women of my age, middle age, and old age, who have such positive strategies, such humour, such self-respect, such imagination, and capacity for endurance and determination, has changed that for me. I am amazed at the richness of women's lives, at the depth of their understanding, at their ingenuity and strength for seeing the way ahead. Although I know society will hit me over the head for not being seventeen, I experience that with a different perspective now, with a greater sense of where my own personal power comes from. Although my body is changing and will continue to change, I feel the grief, the challenge, and the positive aspects of this will be less of a catastrophe and more of a natural part of my movement through my time on this planet. I hope that the shared words of these women and the structured exercises I have given may produce a similar shift for you.

I leave almost the last word of the book to Susan, and add as an epilogue a powerful meditation which helps to reintegrate us at any time when our lives feel out of step.

Susan's point is this:

> I would say to all women thinking about ageing – do not fear it out of hand. I feel more at home in the world now I am older. I feel more aware of my power which is enjoyable. I understand my limitations better and so spend less time banging my head against brick walls. I feel quite alone in trying to find out how a woman like me is going to get older, but it is a challenge.
>
> I am finding it the best part of my life so far.

Epilogue
Meditation on the Great Peace

You can do this meditation on your own or with a partner. If you are going to do the meditation alone, first choose a friend or loved one whose face you are going to call to mind while you meditate; second, read through the meditation several times until you are familiar with the shape of it, and then sit yourself comfortably, with your spine lifting and your shoulders relaxed, and let it gradually unfold in your mind.

If you are going to do the meditation with a partner, similarly, read through it a few times, and then sit comfortably facing one another, either looking into each other's faces for the first two parts, or, if that feels tense and difficult, closing your eyes and visualizing each other's faces for the first two parts.

If you are doing the meditation in a group, sit opposite a partner, as above, either looking into her face, or closing your eyes and visualizing her face for the first two parts. Ask one person to sit separately and read the meditation out slowly, pausing between phrases to allow people to experience how they feel.

Sit comfortably on the floor with your legs crossed or stretched out in front, or if you are sitting in chairs uncross your legs and place your feet on the floor. Sit up tall, lifting through your spine and lifting the crown of your head. Release your shoulders.

Start to breathe a little more deeply and a little more slowly than usual. Hear your breath coming and going in a steady flow. Feel your face and eyes are soft, your limbs heavy and relaxed, your hands gently curled and your feet heavy and soft.

Begin by looking gently into your partner's face. Look carefully but softly, noticing details, as though you had never seen her/his face before.

Now, imagine that you have a task to perform, a project to undertake, a job to do. Imagine that your partner is going to be your ally in this. Still looking softly and attentively, see all the strengths and qualities in your partner that are reflected in her/his face, all the strengths and qualities that will be helpful and empowering to you as you make an effort together.

The feeling that you are feeling now is the *Great Wealth*.

Look again, softly and attentively into your partner's face. Imagine what her/his face must have been like when she/he was very young. See if you can see the child's face within. Now see how time and experience has sculpted and made its tracks, shaped and influenced your partner's face. See how the experiences, happy and sad, fearful and positive, of this person's life, are alive in the face.

The feeling that you are feeling now is the *Great Compassion*.

If your eyes are open, let them close now.

Now drop deep down into yourself, right down into the core of yourself, like a stone dropping down into a well.

As you did with your partner earlier, become aware of the

strengths and qualities which are your own. Deep inside yourself, let yourself know what those strengths and qualities are.

Let yourself become aware of all the wealth of experience in your own life that you have lived through.

And now become aware of the whole web of existence, of living things, the planet, and the universe, all woven together in the great web of life.

Be aware of your own place in the great web of things, which no confusion or misery can ever take away from you, no foolishness or wickedness can ever remove. Be aware of yourself in your own place in the universe.

The feeling that you are feeling now is called the *Great Peace.*

Further Reading

Women's health

Menopause, the Woman's View, Anne Dickson and Nicky Henriques, Thorsons, 1987.
The Captured Womb, Ann Oakley, Blackwell, 1986.
A History of Women's Bodies, Edward Shorter, Pelican, 1982.
No Immediate Danger, Rosalie Bertell, Women's Press, 1985.
The Tentative Pregnancy, Barbara Katz Rothman, Pandora, 1988.
Miscarriage, Ann Oakley et al., Penguin, 1984.

Women's work

Housewife, Ann Oakley, Penguin, 1974.
The Handmaid's Tale, Margaret Atwood, Virago, 1987 (novel).
Out of the Doll's House, Angela Holdsworth, BBC Publications, 1988.
Old Mistresses, Rozsika Parker and Griselda Pollock, Pandora, 1986.
Gyn/Ecology, Mary Daly, Women's Press, 1979.

Women and war

Women in War, Shelley Saywell, Thorsons, 1985.
The Taste Of War, Margaret Bourke, Century, 1985.
Nella Last's War, Sphere Books, 1981.

Physical expression

The Body Has Its Reasons, Thérèse Bertherat, Cedar Press, 1988.

Moving Zen, Karate as a Way to Gentleness, C. W. Nicol, Crompton, 1981.

Women Running, Liz Sloan and Ann Kramer, Pandora, 1986.

The Book of Yoga, Sivananda Yoga Book, Ebury Press, 1983.

Kyudo: The Art of Zen Archery, Hans Joachim Stein, Element, 1988.

The Sensual Body, Lucy Lidell, Unwin Hyman, 1987.

Stretch and Relax, M. Tobias and M. Stuart, Dorling Kindersley, 1985.

Women's Experience of Sex, Sheila Kitzinger, Dorling Kindersley, 1983.

Philosophy/psychology/exploration

In Our Own Hands, Sheila Ernst and Lucy Goodison, Women's Press, 1981.

In Our Experience, Sue Kreowski and Pat Land, Women's Press, 1988.

On Death and Dying, Elisabeth Kubler Ross, Souvenir, 1982.

Zen Practice in Daily Life, Daihin Katigin, Shambhala, 1988.

A Woman on the Edge of Time, Marge Piercy, Women's Press, 1979 (novel).

Taking it Like A Woman, Ann Oakley, Virago, 1984.

The Uses of Enchantment, Bruno Bettelheim, Thames and Hudson, 1976.

Descent to the Goddess, Sylvia Brinton Pevera, Inner City Books, 1981.

A Woman in Your Own Right, Anne Dickson, Quartet, 1982.

Self-defence

Stand Your Ground, Kaleghl Quinn, Macdonald Optima, 1988.

Her Wits About Her, Denise Caignon and Gail Groves, Women's Press, 1989.

Index